THE NATURE
OF SCIENCE
AND
SCIENCE TEACHING

WADSWORTH GUIDES TO SCIENCE TEACHING

edited by
Paul DeHart Hurd, Stanford University

MODERN CHEMISTRY TEACHING
Marjorie Gardner, University of Maryland

TESTING AND EVALUATION FOR THE SCIENCES
William D. Hedges, Clayton Public School District

ISSUES IN JUNIOR HIGH SCHOOL SCIENCE TEACHING
Paul DeHart Hurd, Stanford University

NEW DIRECTIONS IN ELEMENTARY SCIENCE TEACHING
Paul DeHart Hurd, Stanford University, and James Joseph Gallagher,
Educational Research Council of America

CASE STUDY TECHNIQUES IN SCIENCE
Leo E. Klopfer, University of Chicago

NEW DEVELOPMENTS IN SCIENCE TEACHING
Eugene C. Lee, Emory University

THE NATURE OF SCIENCE AND SCIENCE TEACHING
James T. Robinson, Columbia University

THE NATURE
OF SCIENCE
AND
SCIENCE TEACHING

JAMES T. ROBINSON

Columbia University

Wadsworth Publishing Company, Inc.
Belmont, California

L. C. Cat. Card No.: 68–19444
Printed in the United States of America

PREFACE

This book is written for those who are concerned with the relationships between the nature of science and the teaching of science. The importance of these relationships has been recognized so recently that those attempting to study them have had to rely almost entirely upon committee reports and curriculum materials—sources of information that, by their very nature, fail to provide the antecedents of their claims.

The Nature of Science and Science Teaching examines the writings of six scholars, all working scientists, who have given considerable attention to the broader and deeper aspects of science as a field of intellectual inquiry.

The language of the original sources has been preserved as much as possible to avoid any impression that the writer is a specialist in philosophy and to avoid distortion of the essential ideas of these sources. Extensive citations are incorporated into this writing to enable the reader to trace the interpretations back to their original works. This approach is an argument in support of the science educator as a relator of disciplines from which an applied field must draw its substance.

Part 1 explores the growth of scientific knowledge and the problems for science education that this growth has generated. Part 2 presents a detailed discussion of Henry Margenau's *The Nature of Physical Reality,* the most comprehensive work selected in this study. Brief accounts of five works are given in Part 3: Philipp Frank's *Philosophy of Science;* Percy Bridgman's *The Nature of Some of Our Physical Concepts;* Joseph Woodger's *Biology and Language;* Morton Beckner's *The Biological Way of Thought;* and "Concepts of Biology," edited by Ralph Gerard. Part 4 proposes specific considerations for educators in the sciences. The emphasis is upon delineating those understandings about science which would increasingly characterize the thought of individuals intent upon growing in scientific literacy.

The ideas presented in this one book cannot be considered final;

for further investigation and verification of these arguments must precede their use. However, they can bring educators who wish to produce programs of science education that reflect the essential characteristics of scientific knowledge, closer to this goal.

It is my privilege to acknowledge the assistance and encouragement given me by Professor Paul DeHart Hurd, Stanford University, in the investigations which preceded this book.

I also wish to thank the following publishers for granting permission to quote from the cited works: McGraw-Hill Book Company, *The Nature of Physical Reality* by Henry Margenau; Prentice-Hall, Inc., *Philosophy of Science* by Philipp Frank; Philosophical Library, *The Nature of Some of Our Physical Concepts* by Percy W. Bridgman; Cambridge University Press, *Biology and Language* by J. H. Woodger; Columbia University Press, *The Biological Way of Thought* by Morton Beckner; *Behavioral Science,* "Concepts of Biology," edited by Ralph W. Gerard; and the National Education Association, "The Structure of the Disciplines" by Joseph J. Schwab.

CONTENTS

PART 1
THE CHANGING
NATURE
OF KNOWLEDGE
AND THE SCIENCE
CURRICULUM

No course in a science has ever been able to teach all that is known about that science. But, now, the selection of those aspects of the science to be taught is increasingly difficult because of the rapid development of knowledge occurring in every science. Additions of subject matter to courses by the process of accretion have not taken into account the nature of the growth of knowledge in the sciences in the twentieth century. An examination of this growth suggests that new approaches to the development of science curricula are needed if instruction is to reflect a "structure" of science.

1

TOWARD
REDEVELOPMENT
OF SCHOOL
SCIENCE
CURRICULA

The place of the sciences within the school curriculum has shifted dramatically since the turn of this century. From their beginnings, as incidental instruction in nature study and health, the curricula for science education have been expanded to include today what are considered to be the basic, or fundamental, aspects of both the physical and biological sciences.

In 1945 the Harvard Committee, while considering the problems of general education in a free society,[1] formulated this question as its major concern: "How can general education be so adapted to different ages and, above all, differing abilities and outlooks, that it can appeal deeply to each, yet remain in goal and essential teaching the same for all?" The question as it applies to science curricula remains to be resolved. One essential assumption embedded in the question is a reference to a certain, perhaps stable, something that can be adapted to fit the science education needs of all students. The contemporary idiom for this "something" would seem to be the "structure of the disciplines." But what is structure and what are the disciplines? Some answers to these questions have been proposed in recent publi-

---

[1] *General Education in a Free Society,* Report of the Harvard Committee. Cambridge, Massachusetts: Harvard University Press, 1945.

cations.[2] Critics have questioned whether the terms are anything more than new educational slogans.[3]

Jerome Bruner, in reporting on the attention given to the structure of knowledge as a guide to curriculum decision-making, synthesized the thinking of many scholars and educators at the Woods Hole Conference in September 1959. He pointed out that in order to plan curricula that reflect the basic structure of a field of knowledge, one must have a most fundamental understanding of that field. He offers four "claims that can be made for teaching the fundamental structure of a subject, *claims in need of detailed study.*"[4] [Italics mine.] In brief, these claims are that an understanding of structure makes a subject more comprehensible, longer remembered, and more transferable and that it offers the educator the greatest opportunity for narrowing the gap between "advanced" and "elementary" knowledge. It is important here to emphasize the assumptions that fields of knowledge *have* structures that are known and agreed upon and that such structures carry inherent characteristics important for learning.

Joseph Schwab, in both published and unpublished works, has suggested that educators analyze the structure of knowledge and the processes of inquiry for some help in determining what most validly may be taught. In explaining why curriculum makers and teachers should be concerned with the structure of a discipline he states:

Structures are desirable or necessary in the service of three functions. First, structures permit us to discover what *kind* of statement we are dealing with—whether it is a verifiably informative statement, a statement designed to move our emotions, a statement of choice, value or decision, and so on. Second, structures permit us to determine to what degree and in what sense an informative statement is "true." Third, structure permits us to discern more completely or more correctly the meaning of informative statements.[5]

---

[2] *The Structure of Knowledge and the Curriculum,* G. W. Ford and Lawrence Pugno (eds.). Chicago: Rand McNally and Company, 1964; *Education and the Structure of Knowledge.* Stanley Elam (ed.). Chicago: Rand McNally and Company, 1964.

[3] B. Paul Komisar and James E. McClellan, "The Logic of Slogans," in *Language and Concepts in Education.* B. Othanel Smith and Robert H. Ennis (eds.). Chicago: Rand McNally & Company, 1961, 195–215; or, Herbert M. Kliebard, "Structure of the Disciplines as an Educational Slogan," *Teachers College Record,* 66 (April 1965), 598–603.

[4] Jerome S. Bruner, *The Process of Education.* Cambridge: Harvard University Press, 1961, pp. 23–32.

[5] Joseph J. Schwab, "The Structure of the Disciplines." A working paper

It is not difficult to explain the enthusiasm with which educators have welcomed the notion of structure. The very term implies a permanence and stability that has appeal for those working in fields of rapidly expanding knowledge. It also carries the aura of academia. Such is the case for those engaged in science education at all levels. Not only has scientific knowledge increased in quantity, but also, old patterns of thought have been modified in ways that have caused profound changes in scientists' views of natural phenomena.

Nineteenth century science was characterized by an emphasis upon accumulation of data, the classification and description of it, and by an emphasis upon mechanistic modes of interpretation. These modes of thought supported a world view depicting a finite, static, homocentric universe, harmoniously arranged in a hierarchical order. But during the late nineteenth and early twentieth centuries, the pathways of scientific thought departed from these emphases. In the physical sciences, the change began with a new synthesis of knowledge that accompanied the development of the relativity theory, and it was accentuated by the advent of quantum mechanics. In the biological sciences, it began with the interpretation of biological phenomena through the theory of evolution, moved on with the rediscovery of Mendelian genetics, and was accentuated by the growth of molecular biology. The static view of the world was slowly supplanted by one of a restless and apparently boundless universe. These revolutionary changes in scientific knowledge were not immediately accompanied by a parallel shift in instruction in the sciences. As Schwab indicates, the science curricula in the schools have not, until very recent days, reflected the changing nature of scientific knowledge; instead, they have reflected the approaches and methods of earlier science.

The divergence in the nature of the scientific enterprise and the teaching of science was finally recognized by the scientific community in the 1950's, when it initiated a series of curriculum studies—PSSC, CBA, CHEMS, BSCS, and, more recently, ESCP, IPS, and others. Each of these studies has been developed by working scientists, generally in cooperation with school science teachers. Each has provided up-to-date content in the materials developed. All have recognized that some content becomes outdated fast, even by the time of publication. More importantly, each study has recognized the prob-

---

prepared for the Project on Instruction of the National Education Association, p. 9. (Mimeographed.) (Quoted by permission.)

lem of communicating—to the teachers who will use the materials and to science departments in colleges—the rationale and philosophical basis of its materials.

THE GROWTH OF SCIENTIFIC KNOWLEDGE

An understanding of the rapid growth and changing nature of scientific knowledge may help to clarify the problems confronting science education. Such an understanding is important not only for interpreting recent developments in science curricula, but it is also important for developing capabilities that will be needed to cope with changes which will come even more rapidly in the future. Perspective regarding these changes is provided by a brief resumé of the growth of science from the Classical Age to the present, as stated by Gerard Piel.

Until the scientific enterprise began 400 years ago, the rate of invention hugged the time base line. The stock of technique increased by arithmetic progression, as often as not by accident, and without real understanding of the principles involved. For the past three centuries, however, the progression has been geometric, climbing steeply toward parallel with the vertical coordinate. Now invention has entered a new phase. It exploits understanding already established; it responds not merely to necessity but to opportunity presented by new knowledge. Technology will move forward with it.[6]

Robert Oppenheimer and Philip Phenix, among others, have reflected upon this acceleration and growth in knowledge. Oppenheimer, speaking at a conference of the American Academy of Arts and Sciences, emphasized this change by stating:

Actually, in the rapid change, the great discoveries everybody has talked about since the Renaissance, the sum of positive knowledge has increased at an increasing rate. I would even say that it is not fifty years, as was said in the eighteenth century, in which positive knowledge doubles, but something between a decade and a generation. The mass of knowledge grows fantastically; the rate of growth itself grows.[7]

[6] Gerard Piel, "The Revolution in Man's Labor," *Bulletin of the Atomic Scientist,* XV (September 1959), 281.
[7] Robert Oppenheimer, "The Growth of Science and the Structure of Culture," *Daedalus,* LXXXVII, No. 1 (1958), 76.

Phenix, in discussing the organization of knowledge and its growth, explained the reasons behind its rapid development.

Modern man possesses a vast and rapidly expanding supply of knowledge. There are many causes for this, including the persistent application of scientific procedures to the whole compass of human experience, the invention of instruments whereby the precision and range of inquiry have been greatly increased, the explosive growth in world population, with a corresponding rise in the numbers of workers in every field of inquiry, and the provision of extensive libraries and museums for preserving the accumulated treasures of the past.[8]

Focusing on the past twenty to thirty years, N. N. Semenov has reflected on this growth as follows:

Science and technology started their triumphant advance early in the nineteenth century. In the past twenty or thirty years, this progress has acquired exceptional speed, and a previously unheard-of breadth. It is hard to imagine at what breathtaking speed the capacity of man to master the forces of nature may advance in the future. A very real scientific and technological base is being laid for the achievement of any reasonable level of well-being of all mankind.[9]

Because of this acceleration of knowledge, problems arise for the selection of significant curriculum content for science education and for the correlative possibility of "defaults in understanding." This latter idea was commented on by T. Keith Glennan when he wrote:

It is ironic that in this time of lightning swift mechanical and universal communication of thoughts and images, we are threatened with the already massive, and still growing defaults in understanding. In education, politics, sociology, the arts, the sciences, we are approaching a modern Tower of Babel—a state of paralyzing, mutual incomprehension—just as we enter what may be a climactic period of man's career on Earth.[10]

Specialization of knowledge plays a part in what Glennan sees as the possible default of understanding, for, as he states in another context:

[8] Philip H. Phenix, "Key Concepts and the Crisis in Learning," *Teachers College Record,* LVIII (December 1956), 137.
[9] N. N. Semenov, "The Future of Man in the Atomic Age," *Bulletin of the Atomic Scientist,* XV (March 1959), 123.
[10] T. Keith Glennan, "New Order of Technological Challenge," address, December 27, 1959, *Vital Speeches,* XXVI (February 1, 1960), 237.

In science, particularly, the tendency more and more has been to penetrate farther and farther into chosen subjects until specialists dig themselves deep out of sight, out of hearing, out of understanding of what other scientists are doing in their own and neighboring fields. And, if this state of affairs is alarming, even more alarming is the growing cleavage between science and scientists as a whole and the great mass of humanity in other callings.[11]

Susanne Langer, writing in *Philosophy in a New Key,* noted this same concern with specialization when she commented:

Here we run into a difficulty inherent in the scholarship of our time—the obstacle of *too* much knowledge, which forces us to accept the so-called "findings" of specialists in other fields, "findings" that were not made with reference to our searchings, and often leave the things that would be most important for us, unfound.[12]

But the problems growing out of acceleration reside not alone in the great growth of knowledge itself, but in the ability of individuals to deal with this mass of data; for, as Phenix observes,

The crisis in learning consists in this disproportion between what is available and necessary to know and the capacity of the individual to know. This is perhaps the fundamental problem which contemporary education faces. Every person is embarrassed by the wealth of available knowledge which he cannot hope to appropriate.[13]

Along with human capacity as a dimension of the problem of knowing comes the associated problem of the availability of knowledge. As E. D. Adrian and others have observed, our store of knowledge is increasing so rapidly we need to find new ways to make it available.

REDIRECTING SCIENCE EDUCATION

With this explosion in knowledge and the problems related to it—possible inadequacies in understanding, specialization, the ability of the individual to cope with the accumulating mass of material, and the problem of diffusing this knowledge—other writers have turned their attentions to how knowledge may be more efficiently organized.

[11] *Ibid.*
[12] Susanne K. Langer (New York: The New American Library, 1958), pp. 185–6.
[13] Phenix, *op. cit.,* p. 138.

Jacob Bronowski, in setting the stage for solution, wrote that an "educated society can exist only when knowledge is not merely stored, but is common."[14]

But how may the knowledge in science be organized so that a curriculum based upon it can serve the dual needs of "common" knowledge for the many students and "specialized" knowledge for others? How may the "specialized" knowledge be organized and presented so that it imparts some of a "common" total view to those students who will become specialists? One focus of this study is on a search for the "common" knowledge in science that should be a part of the science education of all students. Another focus is upon the framework of ideas which shape and direct the scientific disciplines. Various writers have reflected upon aspects of these problems.

Glennan, in the source cited earlier, suggests that a new discipline may be needed.

Perhaps we need a new look at the activities of man surveyed as an organism. Perhaps we need a new breed of specialists—let me call them "relaters"—men who will devote themselves to the seeking out of effective methods of interrelating the knowledge and work of the physical scientist, the engineer, the political scientist, the humanist and other professional disciplines.

Glennan may be indicating some possible dimensions of changes for the role of the science teacher. Perhaps such teachers will need to be more concerned than they are now with the "interrelating" of knowledge. Perhaps, too, they will need to give greater attention to the organization of knowledge.

Julian Huxley stresses the need for the organization of knowledge.

First let us remember that most of what we can properly call advance in psychosocial evolution has stemmed from new or better-organized knowledge, whether in the form of traditional skills, sudden inventions, new scientific discoveries, technological improvements, or new insights into old problems.[15]

James Killian is critical of current practices in science and K. F. Mather criticizes practices in general education.

[14] Jacob Bronowski, "Knowledge and Education," *Library Journal,* XIV (February 1, 1958), 338.

[15] Julian Huxley, "The Future of Man," *Bulletin of the Atomic Scientist,* XV (December 1959), 403.

It has become clear that too much of the science instruction was either descriptive or technological and that it did not illuminate the most fundamental concepts and views of the universe, which makes physics so basic and powerful a subject—both culturally and in terms of science. I cite this as an example of the importance of re-thinking the content of our school subject matter at the secondary level, not only in the sciences but in other fields, and of achieving a deeper grasp of the great fundamentals which underlie our culture and our professions.[16]

Too much of our so-called "General Education" is concerned with the acquisition of factual data culled from a broad array of sources. It is conceptual thinking that should be stressed; integrative concepts that should be known.[17]

Other writers, having appraised the growth of knowledge, the problems within this growth, and the current state of the organization of knowledge, have turned more specifically to the ways in which knowledge may be more effectively organized.

The criteria of comprehensiveness and discrimination seem to be central to the thinking of Joseph Schwab.

Hence inquiry proceeds along two parallel lines. There is not only creation of knowledge via a chosen set of principles, but, through the same inquiries, a testing which leads to new principles comprehensive of more and more of the richness of the originating subject matter. And with each change of principle, the knowledge gained in terms of the old is reordered into terms of the new.

The revisionary character of scientific knowledge is, then, a quality which accrues from the continuing assessment and modification of principles of inquiry. The cliche that science is cumulative does not mean that one fact is added to another while the pile grows larger, but, rather, that as the growth of knowledge necessitates change of principle, the knowledge contained in older formulations, "right" enough in its own terms and when referred to its restricted subject matter, is replaced by knowledge, not more "right," but more comprehensive, more discriminating, or more nearly exhaustive of the originating subject materials.[18]

Phenix, in discussing the structure of knowledge in his article mentioned earlier, indicates that it is possible to find "key concepts" which are "distinguished by their power to epitomize important com-

[16] James R. Killian, Jr., "Problems of Science Teaching in the United States," *The Challenge of Science Education,* Joseph S. Roucek (ed.) (New York: Philosophical Library, 1959), 429.

[17] K. F. Mather, "Scientist's Responsibility for the Interpretation of Concepts to Laymen," *Science,* CXIX (March 5, 1954), 300.

[18] Joseph J. Schwab, "The Teaching of Science as Inquiry," *Bulletin of the Atomic Scientist,* XIV (November 1958), 375.

mon features of a large number of more particular ideas." But discovering these concepts is not enough for a modern formulation of scientific thought.

Langer illustrates the significance of developing a construct of relationships between these various concepts when she writes:

> But a thousand becomes merely "a great number." Its exact fixation requires an order of concepts in which it holds a definite place, as each number concept does in our number system. But to denote such a host of concepts and keep their relations to each other straight, we need a symbolism that can express both terms and relationships more economically than pictures, gestures, or mnestic signs.[19]

This quotation by Langer contains the germ from which a new approach to the organization of scientific knowledge for the development of science curriculum may come: exactness of understanding, she says, "requires an order of concepts," that will make it possible for any structure which is evolved to keep straight the relations among concepts. From this new approach based upon *an order of concepts* and their *relationships* may come a new point-of-view for the teaching of science.

Each of the writers who have presented aspects of the growth and change within knowledge has, by implication, been focusing upon needed re-thinking of the science curriculum. For while new developments have been accumulating, the tendency in science teaching has been to add new factual content to the traditional courses without facing the essential need to select, from all that is known, that which is most relevant. Thus, courses have become overcrowded with masses of often unrelated data, and teaching procedures have become hurried and frequently unrewarding. The challenge is how to so reorganize the basis of science curricula as to provide learning experiences that encourage students to develop habits of inquiry and a continuing desire to pursue knowledge. For we know that both the young scientist and the young layman of today will find that knowledge which is significant will change several times during his life. Many writers who have reflected upon this problem have indicated that consideration should be given to the nature and organization of knowledge as a possible means of developing greater understanding of the scientific enterprise. Thus, an approach to the development of

[19] Langer, *op. cit.*, p. 72.

science curricula based upon such understanding may prove more fruitful than simply replacing the obsolete and adding more factual material to an already overladen curriculum.

The challenge to science education is to bring to the full range of young people a comprehension of the nature of science as a humanistic enterprise. This task must be accomplished, at acceptable levels, through the curricula of the schools. This is not to slight the non-school educational agencies in our civilization, but is to delineate the domain within which science educators at all educational levels are directly or indirectly concerned. No longer can an understanding of science be relegated to those who devote their lives to scientific pursuits. The pervasiveness of scientific thought throughout our culture is no longer in question. But the realization that important scientific discoveries are never mere additions to knowledge has not been adequately recognized in the educational community. Whether this is an oversight or a desire to avoid responsibility for dealing with the impact of the sciences on society remains obscure. What is no longer obscure is the challenge that new discoveries make to established beliefs and to what is called "common sense." It is also apparent that new knowledge will continue to present pressing social and ethical problems in the future.

Contributions of the *structure* of the disciplines to education have been claimed, but the structures themselves have remained obscure. Next, we shall explore the writings of several scientist-philosophers in a search for possible meanings for structure in the sciences. Writings by physicists and biologists will be examined for those essential elements and relationships within the sciences that make them distinct areas of inquiry. This exploration necessarily includes a discussion of the relevancy of the emergent framework or structure to science education.

The intent of this book is not to provide science educators with a ready-made pattern for the development of science curricula. Rather, it is intended that those concerned with science education will find that a structure of science developed here has significance for curricular development and for the education of science teachers. If the idea of structure is to become more than an educational slogan, the kinds of understandings presented in this exploratory work need serious consideration.

PART 2
A VIEW OF THE
CONSTRUCTIONAL
NATURE
OF PHYSICAL REALITY

The framework of ideas developed by Henry Margenau to characterize the physical sciences is examined extensively in Part 2. Margenau's analysis of physical reality is both comprehensive and precise. As such, it should help those concerned with science curricula to appreciate the complexities of the issues with which they are engaged and to realize the extent of scholarly effort needed to bring about some resolution of these issues.

Margenau's analysis is in general convergence with those of five other authors whose views will be considered in later chapters. However, aspects of the inductive-deductive phases of inquiry are most fully elucidated by Margenau. In the other works that will be examined, induction and deduction are only implied or given brief discussion—particularly in the writings of biological scientists.

Although each of the authors whose writings will be discussed in Part 3 uses different modes of explanation, the essential outline of Margenau's analysis stands forth in their works as a useful pattern of thought. Science educators will find that Margenau's analysis has a direct bearing on questions they must resolve about science curricula and the philosophies of science teaching that are fundamental to curricula.

Both this part, where Margenau's *The Nature of Physical Reality: A Philosophy of Modern Physics* is examined, and Part 3, which examines the works of five other scientists, depend heavily upon the original works. The discussions retain much of the language of the original authors. The parenthetical references liberally inserted throughout these parts document pages of the original works containing the discussions that are paraphrased and direct quotations that are excerpted.

2

THE SCIENTIST
WITH NATURE

Throughout history men have observed the phenomena of Nature and then attempted to explain them. Man's knowledge of such phenomena, observed and explained at different points in time, has gone through a number of interesting phases. For example, the views of Aristotle dominated pre-Newtonian concepts of force. As Margenau points out,[1] "With Aristotle there was no force at all; falling bodies were in natural motion and required no force." His view of mechanics, in which he distinguished between natural and violent motions, was a largely correlational approach to science and, in the view of Margenau, is "unassailable on empirical grounds but is quite unsatisfactory on others." (77)

Aristotle's treatment of the causal problem divided causes into four types—formal, material, efficient, and final—which rendered the problem incapable of solution and shifted the attention of philosophers to partial causes and away from the feature of inevitability. His four-fold list of partial causes was proliferated in the Middle Ages to an extent now considered absurd. This proliferation illustrates the dangers of venturing into searches for partial causes, searches which can never be complete. (395)

But the Middle Ages were built on Aristotle and not on Democritus, who expressed a view of causality in harmony with modern science when he said: "By necessity are foreordained all things that were and are and are to come." During the Middle Ages, physical

[1] Henry Margenau. *The Nature of Physical Reality: A Philosophy of Modern Physics*. New York: McGraw-Hill Book Company, Inc., 1950. Quoted by permission.

description was dominated by the presuppositions of ontology that were based upon the authority of Aristotle as interpreted by his scholastic commentators. A scientific upheaval that took place in the sixteenth and seventeenth centuries, culminating in the works of Newton and Leibniz, emancipated physical doctrine from scholastic ontology. In Margenau's view this emancipation led to "a first frank avowal by natural science of epistemology as the highway to its goal." (307)

THE MECHANISTIC VIEW

The development of Newtonian mechanics was accompanied by the development of the spectatorial doctrine. In Margenau's analysis, "The spectacle envisioned by Newtonian physics is one in which masses move in absolute space and time and are capable of being beheld by mind." The spectator is regarded as an observer standing in a universe and surrounded on all sides by perceptible and perceivable matters of fact. He is a minor part of the universe, and his removal will affect the universe but slightly. If the Newtonian mechanist is asked to separate the spectator from his surroundings, "he is driven back to the citadel of mind as the only spectatorial part of the universe. Mind, or ego, then appears as a singularity in an otherwise regular and continuous structure." (34–35)

The mechanistic view seems to be supported by every disclosure of our senses: "moving masses are seen to move; they are obviously before us in time and space; they occupy definite positions at definite instants of time." It is a view which was challenged in the early days of Newtonian physics by Euler and Kant, who gave early evidence of the "quandaries into which they were thrown by the relativity of the space of mechanics." They perceived early some of the difficulties that were to lead to the viewpoint of modern physics that to see whether one mass moves, "the spectator must now look at another mass as well, for only relative motion is significant." (35–38)

THE MODERN VIEW

The development of quantum mechanics led to the breakdown of the mechanistic view, even though "everyone who believes himself to be an observer in an independent universe and who locates all events and objects uniquely in time and space" retains a mechanistic view-

point. (38) Physicists had developed the habit of correlating data
with mechanical models, for Poincaré was believed to have shown
"that *every* phenomenon could be reduced to some form of model."
This habit persisted long after models had been abandoned in electro-
dynamics and optics. (77) The work of Heisenberg and Dirac forced
the physicist either to give up established laws of nature or to alter his
classical (mechanistic) mode of description. This rejection of classical description by physicists posed problems for philosophers who
created the theory of auxiliary concepts to retain the mode of classical
description. This theory holds that "science, released from the bond-
age of sensory experience, no longer describes reality but makes
'models' of reality which serve only the purpose of explanation and
calculation." Margenau rejects this theory and suggests that "in basic
matters we must discipline our intuition and rely more heavily on
abstract thought." (43–45)

Quantum theory has focused attention on the question, What is the
nature of the immediately given? Margenau states that the immediately given must be sought *within experience.* It is wholly unwarranted to *start* a theory of knowledge with the ontological premise
characterizing the spectator-spectacle distinction. (46)

The experience of physicists with atomic particles, such as the
electron, has revealed serious flaws in the spectator-spectacle relation.
Newer knowledge of science indicates that "the knowing subject
intrudes itself unpreventably into the objective scheme of things."
(52) The reformulation of physical description which takes into
account the reciprocity between the observer and the observation
abandoned the spectator-spectacle relation and acknowledges the effect of knowing upon the known.

The modern view, which has grown up in the period since the
formulation of quantum mechanics, places its emphasis upon the
theoretical mode of analysis and upon deductive logic. While no
science is "wholly correlational or wholly deductive . . . the character of a given discipline may partake predominantly of one method or
the other." Margenau finds the trends in the sciences to be toward the
theoretical. (30–31) The impetus toward this direction came with
quantum mechanics, which shunned all models and required an entire
reformulation of physical description. It was founded upon the concept of the "latent observable," and the meaning of reality centered in
the states of the systems. "According to the uncertainty principle, the
act of observation has an important effect upon the observed." (38)

Quantum mechanics posed such challenging questions as these to the world view which had preceded it:

Quantum theory is meaningless without a clear understanding of what, precisely, is immediately given. For if the physical investigator were undeniably *given* such facts as the position and velocity of particles—to cite a famous example—how can the uncertainty principle deny their observability under any circumstances? If time is given immediately in sensation, how can the physicist make theories that fashion time after abstract mathematical patterns? (52)

These were basic problems and it is to these and others that Margenau addresses his analysis. In his discussion of sense data of interest to science, he develops unique criteria for discerning between objective and nonobjective data, and he devotes major attention to the universally accepted formalism for rationalizing sense data that characterizes modern physical science. (50)

REALITY

The nature of physical reality, as developed by Margenau, is one that rejects the idea of the absolutely permanent. Many epistemological fiascoes, he says, are caused by an attempt to implant into reality the notion of the absolutely permanent. (288)

Margenau indicates a belief that a static, unchanging, view of reality is largely the result of investigations which remain wholly within the limits of logical analysis. To him logic seems to say, "Give me the objects of experience and I will define reality." The central question then becomes "What are the objects of experience?" Margenau finds a misunderstanding embedded in a view that reality is the *cause* of our experience. He finds that those who hold this view are unwilling to entertain a formulation of reality which does not explain the whole of human experience. But Margenau sees reality itself as a specifiable part of experience. (288–289)

This description carries with it the implication that there are aspects of experience which are not part of physical reality; an implication which is granted. But Margenau argues that such experience needs to be explored by many methods available to serious scholars in fields other than the sciences. Prior to such analyses, it would seem pardonable that the designation of reality be witheld from them. When these aspects of experience are organized, they may or may not display the characteristics of science.

It is central to this argument that clarification of what is "real" and what is "not real" be attained; for the real must meet certain agreed upon formalisms of construction and verification which will be discussed in the next chapter.

Verifacts are what Margenau calls the elements of physical reality, and there are relations used in establishing verifacts which are neutral with respect to physical reality.

relations between constructs, such as purely logical relations of implication or contradiction, or quantitative relations, such as equality, being greater than, and so forth, should not be regarded as verifacts themselves. One must conceive of them as being neutral with respect to the question of reality. The same is true of the regulative principles [metaphysical principles] . . . ; while their bearing upon reality is very important, they do not claim to being real themselves. (304–305)

The physically real is characterized by durability and permanence but it avoids unreasonable demands for eternal persistence. The reality thus defined is dynamic—it grows and changes as our understanding grows and changes. "Physical reality is not synonymous with concreteness, as that term is ordinarily understood." Margenau's epistemology acknowledges only experience, but

the field of sense data, while coinciding partly with the real domain, does so more or less by pretension; it is unable to demonstrate its relevance by its own indigenous character. For this reason, and for others . . . , we are driven beyond the confines of Nature in our quest for physical reality. (291)

Immediate sense data, or sensory impressions, rules of correspondence, and constructs are the elements of experience significant for science. The processes by which valid constructs—which might be called elements of the real world—are built up must be delayed, but it is important to note that constructs

are not valid because they refer to something real; they denote something real because they have been found valid. . . . Reality is conferred jointly by the process of fitting new parts into an already existing structure of ordered conceptions and by the process of empirical validation. Valid constructs, verifacts in short, are the elements of reality. (292)

Validation of constructs is accomplished by subjecting them to the demands of certain metaphysical requirements, and to the processes of empirical confirmation. Usefulness, the pragmatist's criterion, is insufficient for establishing reality, but it may confer reality when suitably linked with sensory experience. The positing of a second kind of reality, ultimate reality, is not, in Margenau's view, a scientific construct. He sees it as a "hopeful kind [of reality], definable only in retrospect when (and if) science has attained a sufficient degree of convergence." (290–296)

The real world developed by Margenau "comprises all valid constructs and that part of Nature which stands (or stood, in the wider sense which includes historical reality) in epistemic correlation with them." (299) Even though realism, "usually in some inarticulate and non-specific form that is disturbed by finer distinctions, is the philosophy of the working scientist," it is rejected in its simpler conceptions because of its inability to represent correctly such parts of scientific experience as electrons and photons. In its projecting of parts of scientific experience beyond the confines of experience, it "leaves science without defense against fairies, ghosts, and goblins." (457)

An important part of the development of science has been the relationship of man the observer to the natural phenomena he observes. The Aristotelian world view, with its organismic interpretations, was replaced by the spectator-spectacle doctrine of classical mechanics. Investigations into the submicroscopic realm have shattered this conception and required the scientist to reexamine the relationships of observer to observed. This reexamination led Henry Margenau into investigations of the relations between immediate experience and rational thought. In this chapter the origins of the problem of defining these relations have been briefly explored. The succeeding chapters in Part 2 will consider in detail the nature of construction, the development of verifacts, and the nature of physical reality as presented by Margenau.

3

THE ANALYSIS
OF PHYSICAL
REALITY

THE IMMEDIATELY GIVEN

Margenau has developed a framework of ideas by which he attempts to describe the nature of physical reality.[1] He holds with Kant that "epistemology must precede ontology and that epistemology denotes the methodology of the cognitive process." (81) Margenau's epistemology begins with an analysis of experience. As a prelude to this analysis, he rejects the *a priori*, because "science has made continued inroads into the *a priori;* it has taught us the danger of forming unqualifiable beliefs about experience." (62) Experience, as used by Margenau, includes thought, conjecture, and feeling as well as sensation. He rejects the dualism of Locke, the *a priori* significance of elements of experience of Kant, and the stabilization of experience attained by thought of God as developed by Berkeley. (47–48)

Experience

Two perceptive phases of experience are briefly alluded to by Margenau. There is the passive phase, which is uninterpreted sensory perception, and the active phase, which Margenau discusses as it relates to modern physical science. But his emphasis is upon experience, and the discussion of perception becomes a part of the discussion of experience.

[1] Henry Margenau, *The Nature of Physical Reality: A Philosophy of Modern Physics* (New York: McGraw-Hill Book Company, Inc., 1950). Quoted by permission.

Margenau finds that sensory perceptions are the irreducible resid-uums of experience. They are the truly immediate, and they reside at that level of experience which transcends analysis. They cannot figure in physical theories, and they must be rationalized before they can be discussed. Such residuums can be the source of thought and the terminus of expectation. They are that "sensory part of seeing a tree . . . which remains when all rational aspects and all mnemonic associations are deleted from that experience." In thus characterizing sensory perceptions, Margenau indicates an equivalence between the terms "sense data" and "sensory perceptions." However, his further development of his ideas of that experience which is of interest to science indicates that certain sense data have the greater utility and interest for modern physical science; for the sensory data singled out by science for consideration are those that meet the universally ac-cepted formalism for rationalizing data by which the objectivity of the data can be certified. (49–50)

Sense Data

While including those aspects of perception noted above, the sense data, termed "Nature" by Margenau, are those data from which "transition always is made to orderly, conceptual knowledge." (64) A sense datum is an element within the stream of experience which is "distinguished from others by its *spontaneity,* by its relative *independ-ence* from other elements, by its *irreducibility.*" (49)

To the degree that spontaneity is discussed by Margenau, it would seem to characterize sensory data which arrive at the threshold of perception without conscious rational intervention; for if there were such intervention, the movement would have been made from the realm of Nature to that of construction. This spontaneity, however, may arrive within a context of rational relations, but such a context does not endow the elements of perception with a rational character. Independence of elements would seem to be as stated: an independ-ence which allows the datum to be "thought or represented in mem-ory and yet declares itself to be unmistakably different from thought and representation." The greatest measure of Margenau's analysis deals with the characteristic of irreducibility. In its most succinct statement, the residuums, or irreducible qualities of sensory percep-tion, are those perceptions which must be rationalized before they can be discussed at all or before they can figure in physical theories. (49)

But the irreducible qualities do not by themselves distinguish those sense data that are significant to science from those that are not; for these qualities do not distinguish bona fide sense impressions from "sudden pain, dreams, hallucinations, and optical illusions." (50) These latter, too, are sense data, but they may, or may not, have significance for science. While the boundary between sensory data and constructs is not clear, Margenau does make it clear that the modern physical scientist is interested in those data from which transition can be made to orderly conceptual knowledge about physical reality. He says that "What is evident from such considerations is that the field of sense data, while coinciding partly with the real domain, does so more or less by pretension; it is unable to demonstrate its relevance by its own indigenous character." (291)

Prior discussion has indicated that the search for physical reality leads scientists beyond the confines of Nature. However, before proceeding to a discussion of the processes in the constructional realm, we need some additional description of those parts of experience that may become significant in science.

Elements of Experience of Significance for Science

Experience, in Margenau's definition, includes thoughts, conjectures, feelings, and sensations, some of which are not normally standardized into scientific knowledge. Physical reality is a specifiable part of experience and it is characterized by certain aspects of experience that are significant for science: (1) immediate sense data, or impressions, whose totality is called Nature; (2) rules of correspondence; and (3) constructs. (290) The characteristics of sense data have been discussed above, and the rules of correspondence and constructs will be discussed later in this chapter. Since, however, the valid and nonvalid aspects of the immediately given are determined by appealing to principles which do not themselves seem to be furnished by sense data, it is important first to discuss the regulating ideas, or the metaphysical principles.

METAPHYSICAL PRINCIPLES

The evolution of knowledge develops within an explanatory framework which, through metaphysical principles and rules of correspondence, provides the constructs that constitute reality with "a consistency and a logical fertility which sense data alone do not confer." (99) Thus, metaphysical principles are an important part of all procedures which ultimately define physical reality.

These principles do not come from the sense world but are imposed on experience by reason. Such "imposing" is in the nature of "fitting" rather than of "constraining." While the principles are independent of sensory data, Margenau does not find it meaningful to see them as prior to perception, and he rejects conceiving of them as *a priori* postulates of thought. These principles originate "in the stream of experience as tentative expedients, grow into implicit beliefs with increasing implication, and finally, strengthened by repeated success, pervade the entire texture of our theories about the world." Concerning the general characteristics of the principles, Margenau says that "while they are independent of spontaneous experience, they are nevertheless part of, and are stabilized by, experience as a whole. Yet we believe there *can* be experience without them." (79–81)

Margenau indicates that metaphysical principles are not predetermined for all time and, thus, are not immutable. He points to the earlier theories of the nature of scientific knowledge as evidence that the principles slowly change and bring about profound changes in the detailed structure of science. Among his illustrations are the postulate of St. Thomas Aquinas of the compatibility of revelation and scientific method, the insistence of Descartes on the identity of what is formally established with what is materially perceived, the *a priori* conditions of knowledge developed by Kant, and the belief of Maxwell in the ultimacy of mechanical models as symbols of explanation. (81)

Margenau lists six metaphysical principles which he says contribute to the production of acceptable theories. While he discusses these principles independently, as they will be discussed in this presentation, he stresses that they are not cellular; they overlap and interrelate. (82) These six principles are:

A. The Requirement of Logical Fertility
B. The Requirement of Multiple Connections
C. The Requirement of Permanence and Stability
D. The Requirement of Extensibility of Constructs
E. The Requirement of Causality
F. Simplicity and Elegance

The Requirement of Logical Fertility

Modern physical science looks with favor upon those theories having the greatest logical fertility, provided that the other metaphysical requirements are also met.

Once constructs have met the requirement of logical fertility, they can be logically manipulated—that is, they obey logical laws (have relational meanings). That is not to say, however, that propositions involving constructs shall be materially true or have existential counterparts. It only means that constructs so constituted have such proper relational meanings as to allow their utilization in propositions which are in process of empirical verification. (99)

Constructs having logical fertility may enter into propositions as subjects or predicates, as particulars or universals, or as terms which may include, contradict, or imply one another. The formal connections which make possible the establishment of relationships between constructs are stable only so long as certain postulates are maintained. In this sense, all epistemic and constitutive relations are hypothetical until such time as these relations and their constructs have undergone empirical verification and the constructs have qualified as verifacts. After physical laws have been empirically verified, they can be stated as universal propositions that can be applied to particular instances—for example, mass, molecule, chromosome, number. (82–84)

The Requirement of Multiple Connections

Constructs enter into relations with one another through both formal and epistemic definitions. Figure 1 illustrates these relations in

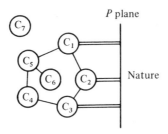

Figure 1. *Relations among constructs.*

Source: Henry Margenau, *The Nature of Physical Reality* (New York: McGraw-Hill Book Company, Inc., 1950), p. 85. Used by permission.

a simplified manner. The double lines connecting constructs with Nature express epistemic definitions which are "equivalent to and . . . [arise] from a rule of correspondence." The relations between the weight of an object and a reading on a scale or between a wavelength and the discernment of a line on a photographic plate are examples of epistemic connections.

The single lines in Figure 1 represent formal connections—

definitions which link construct to construct in a purely logical relationship. Examples of formal connections are the relations between force and acceleration of a given mass, or the relations between the curvature of space and the quantity of matter in the universe. (84)

Constructs which are connected with other constructs or with Nature in such a way that passage elsewhere is possible in at least two ways are described as *multiply connected*. C_1, C_2, C_3, C_4, and C_5 in Figure 1 are examples of multiply connected constructs. Since C_6 possesses only one connection with a normal construct, it is referred to as a "peninsular" construct. Margenau indicates that the color of an electron is an example of a "peninsular" construct—"there is no way of substantiating this attribute, for it leads to no other significant knowledge by any formal route, nor does it allow verification by any possible rule of correspondence." C_7 represents an insular construct; it has no connection with other constructs. Since insular constructs have no connections with other constructs or with Nature, they have no place in science. The God of deism is such a construct. Several insular constructs may be linked together to form an "island universe." Such a universe is consistent in itself but is not verifiable. Although science sometimes generates such systems, the systems do not become a part of science unless rules of correspondence can be found to give them meaning. (85–86)

Margenau points out very carefully, however, that normal constructs do not need to have one connection with Nature (as in C_4 or C_5). Every element of a physical theory does not need to have a counterpart in Nature, but it must always be possible to pass from an accepted construct, *via* other constructs, to Nature in order to meet the requirement of multiple connections. (88)

Every construct used in natural science will be seen to be of this type, permitting passage elsewhere in at least two ways. For example, from the idea of an electron one can pass to its mass, its charge, its field. From its electric field one can go in one direction to the idea of potential, in other directions to certain observable aspects of experience. (86)

The Requirements of Permanence and Stability

Although the physical reality developed by Margenau is a changing one, constructs must meet the metaphysical requirements of permanence and stability. These metaphysical qualities of constructs are not absolute; rather, they extend over the lifetime of a given theory. As a consequence of these requirements, "the *theoretical* components of experience are taken to be sharply defined and uniquely determinable, whereas the *immediate* ones are subject to defects of clarity." The components of theory, constructs and rules of correspondence, remain what they are ". . . so long as the premises of the theory are accepted." (88–89)

In concluding his discussion of permanence and stability, Margenau states:

the constructs generated in explanation of a set of immediate experiences must, so long as the theory of which they form a part is accepted, be used with utmost respect for their integrity of meaning in all applications. They are to be treated as logically clear and sharp entities which may or may not correspond to clear and certain empirical situations. (90)

The Requirement of Extensibility of Constructs

Particular stress is placed upon the regulative value of the requirement of extensibility. In a rather extended discussion of it, Margenau illustrates the necessity for science to look carefully at its metaphysical principles and the role they have played in the development of science. He expresses the idea that through giving particular attention to the requirement of extensibility of constructs, the tendency might be curbed to try to find special laws for special physical domains—the looking for special laws of Nature on different scales of magnitude. Vitalism and the stimulus-response relation are cited as examples of constructs which apply only to living things and, hence, violate the requirement of extensibility. (92–93)

In discussing some of the particular characteristics of extensibility, he indicates that the range of application of a theory is used as a measure not only of its usefulness but also of its credibility. As an illustration of the way in which new theories replace old as the new provide greater extensibility, he traces the development of theories regarding the universe from Galileo through Newton to Einstein, in whose work gravitation ceases to have a status of its own and now appears as an instance of a more extensible construct: the curvature of space-time. In chemistry, Margenau illustrates the greater extensibility of Heitler's quantum interaction between electrical charges over the previously held concept of the valence bond; the newer construct includes the former in a more embracing explanatory scheme. (90–92)

Constructs are extensible in two ways. In one direction they reach out to Nature, and in another direction they reach out to other constructs. The construct "energy" can be identified with many empirical data, such as moving bodies, electricity, and light. The construct "kinetic energy" illustrates the way in which a construct may be related to two other constructs—in this instance kinetic energy states a relation between the constructs energy and velocity. (93–94)

The way in which newly found equivalences may result in new constructs which extend the range of application of previous constructs is illustrated by Margenau in his discussion of Einstein's mass-energy relation. In Einstein's formulation, every mass is equivalent to a proportional amount of energy. Thus, the idea of mass has been extended to include energy, or, by the same token, the idea of energy has been extended to include mass.

Margenau concludes his discussion of extensibility with the following statement:

> At this point, the requirement of extensibility shows a close affinity to . . . the requirement of multiple connections. Both are satisfied in the same creative act, for, while Einstein merely introduced a new relation, that relation happened to be one of equivalence which allowed the merger of two constructs and hence the extension of either. The greatness of this discovery comes from the unusual way in which it satisfies a metaphysical drive and is felt instinctively by every scientist. (94)

The Requirement of Causality

Within the discussion of metaphysical requirements, causality is presented in only a preliminary manner. A full discussion is delayed because of the number of technical problems which must be considered. Following Margenau's pattern, we shall at this point consider only those aspects of causality developed in his preliminary discussion. Causality is regarded as: "a relation between constructs, in particular as a relation between *states,* or conditions, of physical systems. The principle of causality asserts that a given state is invariably followed, in time, by another specifiable state." (95)

Causality is represented by the statement "if *A,* then *B."* In this sense,

> lightning is a condition of the atmosphere describable in terms of physical quantities, such as electric field strengths, ion densities, excitation of atoms and molecules, luminosity. . . . There exist laws by means of which another condition of the same medium, described as thunder and characterized by other measurable quantities, *e.g.,* rhythmic variation in density, can be inferred as the consequent of the first condition. If this condition is

verified sufficiently often, the laws are said to be valid and are said to be *causal laws.* (95)

In thus stating the characteristics of causality, Margenau has neces-sarily ruled out historic interpretations, such as Aristotle's four causes, or the "fortyfold proliferation of causes that occurred in the seventeenth century." A further clarification of causality as a relation patterned after "if *A,* then *B*" is indicated when he states that

certain obscurities in this relation . . . need to be clarified. Above all it must be stated whether *A* and *B* represent immediate experiences, *i.e.,* data, or constructs; if the latter, then whether they are *objects* or *states* of objects. Also, the ambiguity inherent in "if" and "then" is to be elimi-nated, for it is perhaps not clear without comment whether these are to be taken in a conditional or a temporal sense. (94–95)

In developing the idea of causality as stated in the first paragraph of this particular discussion, one finds that the obscurities have been clarified and that the causal relation is concerned with states and within a temporal sense. A further elucidation of the characteristics of causality reveals that causality holds with respect to states defined in terms of significant variables only. Margenau finds two virtues in this formulation, in that, first, it is precise and definite and reflects the best practices in the exact sciences and, second, the more customary forms of causality can always be reduced to this set of stated relations.

According to Margenau, empiricists view causality as an over-whelmingly frequent succession of experiences, a view he considers to be inadequate for modern physical theory in its reference to experi-ence. In the illustration of the states through which lightning and thunder relate to one another, he points out that if the conditions (states) are verified sufficiently often, "the laws are said to be valid and are said to be *causal laws.* Truly, then, causality is a property of physical laws and not of observations." (95–96) This, then, is Mar-genau's repudiation of the empiricists' interpretation of causality as a statement of relations between observables.

Building on from his own formulation of the nature of causality, Margenau argues that this metaphysical requirement "demands that constructs shall be so chosen as to *generate causal laws.*" In discuss-ing the impact of quantum analysis on the causal postulate which he presents, Margenau states that there is no need to revise his postula-tion in view of these new developments; for, although quantum mechanics has taught science to deny a strict causal relation between immediate perceptibles, the work of Heisenberg and Born has shown the "unexpected properties the *states* of physical systems must possess in order to be causally related." (96)

Simplicity and Elegance

Margenau includes the principle of simplicity as a "bow to history," as this issue has probably been accounted for by the principles of multiple connections and extensibility. "When two theories present themselves as competent explanations of a given complex of sensory experience, science decides in favor of the 'simpler' one." (96–97)

The Copernican system replaced the geocentric system because it was simpler. It had special appeal because it reduced the number of epicycles from 83 to 17. There are, however, few examples from the history of science that are as clear cut as this. "Our inability to count ideas, which makes the simple so elusive, also prevents a discrete, nonoverlapping classification of our methodological principles." Simplicity somehow expresses the totality of all the metaphysical principles in concert and has been avowed by scientists throughout the history of science. Margenau calls it "a plain confession of faith on the part of those who seek scientific knowledge." (97–98)

Summary

In this discussion Margenau has contended that the principles directing scientific inquiry do not come to us out of the sense world, and yet they function in guiding experience. It is proper to say that they guide the selection of those aspects of sensory experience which may be linked by rules of correspondence to the rational realm of constructs. Metaphysical principles are not predetermined for all time by our organs of knowledge; their immutability is a myth. It is true, however, that metaphysical principles change relatively slowly and that a slight change in them occasions profound modifications in the detailed structure of science. The metaphysical requirements are a formal sort of demand upon constructs. This demand requires that every explanatory system possess a consistency and logical fertility which sense data alone do not confer. These requirements are presented by Margenau as not being wholly distinct but as blending together into a system which may be called the logic of theoretical science.

RULES OF CORRESPONDENCE

The rules of correspondence have evolved with the growth of knowledge and have been an integral part of this growth process. They are not to be discovered as eternal elements in the nature of experience. They have evolved and they are alterable. The passage from the immediately given in Nature to its constructional counterpart is the epistemic linkage provided by the rules. The terminology for this linkage, described by F. S. C. Northrop as "epistemic correlations," coincides with Margenau's usage, in that those definitions which serve as these linkages are called epistemic. Such definitions are equivalent to and arise from rules of correspondence which link constructs with data. Margenau indicates that the term "rule" is a misnomer, but he has used the term in an attempt to avoid mystifying, although he recognizes the danger of misleading. (62–64)

The rules of correspondence do not have epistemic content of their own; that is, they do not confer validity upon knowledge in and by themselves. "They have to be considered within a larger context of method before they become significantly epistemic, and their acceptance is determined by the functioning of the conceptual apparatus which they generate." (63)

Margenau indicates that we cannot be sure that our present methods, which are described under the sub-section "Examples," have any likelihood of being ultimate. The rules serve as "mental habits," or factors, in establishing reality, but they are not real themselves. They assist scientific discovery by serving as selectors of those sense perceptions which will be considered by science. They function in the role of determining which constructs will be admissible in science; for those which are admissible must be multiply connected and thus must stretch one "arm" toward Nature and one toward the other constructs. (85–87)

With this brief overview of the methodological significance of the rules, a more thorough review of their characteristics will be of value.

Characteristics

In discussing the characteristics of the rules, Margenau describes their somewhat elusive and, yet, most essential nature. Their elusiveness is stated in such references as "the rules are not unique . . . , relations . . . cannot always be stated except by reference to the terms they relate; they are often simply passages . . . their range of application is also difficult to specify." (60–62) Such statements indicate the difficulty of verbalizing this first movement from immediate sense data to rationalized knowledge, but even considering this difficulty of verbalization, the importance of this methodological step cannot be overlooked; for while the rules cannot determine whether or not what they define is physically acceptable, they do provide science with the cognitive process for positing aspects of nature of concern to it. (75) In discussing the role of rules of correspondence in relation to the metaphysical requirements of permanence and stability, Margenau states:

Uncertainty of identification can arise only as a result of ambiguities in the immediate experience, not through an available choice of rules of correspondence. These rules are clear and unequivocal in their action once they have become maxims of experience. It is, therefore, improper to assert that a given complex of sense data relates to objects with probability only, that one rule has a greater chance of being correct than others. The *theoretical* components of experience are taken to be sharply defined and uniquely determinable, whereas the *immediate* ones are subject to defects of clarity. (89)

Thus we see that the rules of correspondence are theoretical components of experience, but in their epistemic relation they always maintain one "leg" in Nature. They are "clear and unequivocal in their action."

Functions

As important parts of every theory of nature, the rules of correspondence play the methodological role of taking knowledge from bare sensory fact to a domain in which logical processes are possible. In this role they link Nature to "entities which we have vaguely termed concepts, ideas, reflective elements, and so forth." (68–69)

As Margenau's exposition develops, we find that the rules of correspondence function in linking sensation, defined as the immediately given, with constructs. Among those closest to Nature, but residing in the constructional realm, are the observable properties. It is these properties which form the essential components of more encompassing constructs, but they themselves are also constructs. As the forthcoming discussion of examples of rules of correspondence will indicate, modern physical science is based upon the mathematical assessment of two types of observable properties—property observables and latent observables. These measurable entities—these observable properties—are absolutely essential components of physical theory and upon their unambiguity rests, in part, the relative surety of our modern knowledge. Margenau indicates that upon the concept of the latent observable rests the whole theory of quantum mechanics, and the rules of correspondence provide the methodological link between the immediately given and the constructed latent observable. (172–174)

> The φ function is a property of an electron just as truly as the blue color is a property of the sky. It is a physical quantity in the same sense as a wavelength or an electric field. And it corresponds to aspects of Nature. But the correspondence, while perfectly unambiguous, is highly instrumental, selective, and refined. (68)

Further discussion by Margenau of state (φ) functions in modern physical theory indicates another aspect of the rules of correspondence—that they may not link single sensory experiences with a single construct. In this context, Margenau writes:

> Notice, too, how another unusual feature has made its appearance. A φ function is related by rules of correspondence, not to a single event in Nature, but to many. *All* the counter responses are synthesized via the rule into *one* state function, and the synthesis involves the idea of probability. (68)

Here then we see a very sophisticated application of the rules of correspondence in the probability synthesis as applied to state functions. This may be the rules performing in their most modern role. But what of other examples of the rules?

Examples

In discussing the various ways in which the passage is made from sensory data to orderly knowledge, Margenau cites five such passages as illustrative of the ways in which the rules operate.

The first example presented involves the operation of the process of reification. Reification is the "act of postulating a *thing* in the face of certain *sensory evidence.*" The external object, such as "tree," cannot be certified by the "rules" alone, but requires the documentation which ". . . refers to the coherence of our entire experience." In this process it is essential to ". . . distinguish between a rule that reifies and the larger part of our experience that objectifies." (64) Thus, a postulating, through reification, of "tree" involves two phases in the cognitive process: integration and construction. The physical object tree emerges as a construct as a result of integration (which includes the seen object, memory, the not remembered, and the not known) functioning within the metaphysical requirement of permanence via the rule of correspondence termed reification. In Margenau's words,

> The act of reification of data involves more than integration: it involves *construction*, construction in accordance with rules. Objectivity emerges as a result of this procedure; to *assert* objectivity is our way of acknowledging the success of the transition from data to the rational wholeness of constructed objects. . . .
> Furthermore, objective things change in a manner somehow conformable to data and therefore can lay no claim to temporal invariance. . . . The known character of an object determines what future sense data are possible quite as much as these determine the object. (59–60)

Thus, the most primitive of the rules of correspondence, reification, functions to postulate the external object through the processing of this rule within the metaphysical requirements and in coherence with our entire experience.

A second example of a passage from Nature to a postulated thing is when the thing "is endowed with specific qualities of its own, qualities which are not 'read from data.' " Typical of such passages is the assignment of mass to bodies. "Mass, though not part of Nature, has some intuitable aspects; but it lies somewhat farther from Nature than does the apple." Energy, light, and force are similarly intuitable qualities and their characteristics often "delude us into thinking that they are data." Adoption of such ideas as mass and the assignment of the qualities that characterize it to bodies leads the scientist into rational territory "where theoretic procedures are possible, which are not possible among the bare elements of Nature." (64–65)

A third example of a rule of correspondence presented by Margenau is highly instrumental. Such a rule would be that which provides for the correspondence between color and wavelength. In their instrumental characteristics they exemplify the special type of rules of correspondence which Bridgman terms "operational definitions." They lead to concepts which are not very obviously related to their perceptible counterparts. (63–66)

A fourth example takes one farther into the constructional realm. In these instances, the rules are highly complex, involving both instrumental manipulations and mathematical processes. Typical of such a passage from data to constructs would be "field strength." The force relationship by which two bodies repel one another is difficult to visualize. In the operation of such rules of correspondence, one is working with elements of Nature neither of which, bodies or force, is found in immediate sensation. (66–67)

Margenau's fifth example is illustrative of the rules functioning in such a way that conditions occur in which the physicist asserts the presence of electrons. In this example, Margenau discusses the way in which probability functions as a rule. As a first step in application of the rule, the state function must be so defined that "the squares of its absolute values shall be identical with the observed probabilities." With the state thus prepared, an electron is found at various points in space. (68–70)

Summary

In these five examples Margenau moves from the simple act of postulating an external thing, reification, to the most precise mathematical utilization of the rules. Each of these passages to constructs is guided by rules of correspondence. In conclusion Margenau states:

The rules of correspondence, it is held, are not eternally grounded in the nature of things, nor are they immediately suggested by sensory experience; they are important parts of every theory of nature and receive their validity from the consistency, the internal neatness and success of the entire explanatory scheme. (73)

CONSTRUCTS

Rules of correspondence link Nature with constructs. In discussing the nature of rules of correspondence and their function in Margenau's epistemology, we have referred to constructs but have delayed an extended discussion of the way in which Margenau uses this term. As this discussion of the evolution of knowledge has progressed, the place of constructs has become more evident. It is important to study the nature of constructs and their function in defining physical reality.

Rules of correspondence lead to a particular tree or a particular electron. Such entities can hardly be called concepts, yet they do partake of the character of concepts and ideas by being rational and

by submitting themselves to logical procedures in a much fuller measure than do the data of Nature. These entities—constructs—are not
found ready-made but have many of the qualities of inventions.
Constructs are not derived from sensory perception. "They come into
their own through what are felt to be creative processes in our
experience rather than through passive contemplation." (69–70)

Trees and electrons, as external objects, are constructs. As such,
they hold the key to physical reality. "The tree is real because it is the
rational terminus of certain rules of correspondence having their
origin in sense impressions and because it satisfies the demands of
consistency which common sense imposes." (292) Not all constructs
are of scientific importance, however. The designation construct is
used "to assign to trees, electrons, ghosts, and devils merely their
correct genetic status in experience." But trees and electrons, in
contrast to ghosts and devils, are more than inventions. They are not
compounded alone from sense data past and present. They also
contain rational elements which point beyond all aspects of immedi-
acy that go into their making. Trees and electrons are *valid* constructs
and, according to Margenau, "it is the principle business of a methodology of science, and indeed of all epistemology, to investigate what
requirements a construct must satisfy to be admitted as valid."
(70–71) Valid constructs do not "owe their existence to accident or
caprice but stand in uniform correlation with immediate experience;
and after their birth they are subject to a most rigorous regime of
methodological principles." (99)

There are both valid and nonvalid constructs. The history of science is replete with instances of provisional constructs which were
developed under assumed rules of correspondence and were suggested
by sense data. Phlogiston and the ether are two well-known examples.
Another obvious example is "that of the sensory experience 'water'
[which] was correlated with a geometric figure . . . by Pythagoras,
with smooth atoms by Democritus, and is at present correlated with
the formula H_2O and with all that it implies." (75)

Valid constructs, or verifacts, are separable into observable properties and systems by Margenau. Observable properties are carried by
systems. As previously mentioned, observable properties may be of
two types: property observables and latent observables. Property
(possessed) observables are assigned when the specific content of
similar observations does not change. In particle mechanics, six possessed properties of a mass point are necessary to ascertain future or

past positions of the particle. Three properties are coordinates of momentum, and three are coordinates of position. (172–201)

No matter how the point [particle] moves, if in a very small interval of time a number of observations on its position and on its momentum are made, they will all yield nearly the same values of x, the same values for y, for z, and also for each of the components of momentum. (179)

At the level of ordinary discourse, it does no harm to consider that a property observable is possessed. For example, the color of a flower may be said to be possessed by the flower, since repeated observations produce the same perception. However, Margenau takes care to develop the relationship of observable to object. He rejects the statement "the flower is blue" for the designation "the blue flower." The observable "blue" is a kind of abstract quality. "The flower is invested with an *observable,* named color. It does not have this color at all times but yields it when it is seen." Where the observable invariably yields the same specific content, in this case "blue," the latency of the observable can be overlooked. In those areas of study in which visualization of phenomena is possible, or when quantities in the ordinary sense of measurement may be assigned, we are dealing with property observables which may be assigned by rules of correspondence. This is true even though one recognizes that the constructed object yields these observables through the process of perception and, in ordinary language, we say they are possessed by the constructed object. (175)

In discussing property observables, Margenau has referred to their "latency" in the sense that they are constructed as a result of perception. However, this sense of "latency" is quite distinct from the qualities of the latent observable. Latent observables, as distinct from property observables, take on different values on different occasions. They seem to take a definite value only by the interaction with an observer. As one moves into fields where visualization fails (quantum mechanics) or where probability measurements are essential (again in quantum mechanics) the role of the latent observable becomes apparent. "Atomic and subatomic objects are like a flower which changes its appearance on repeated instances of looking; observables take on different values on different occasions and are yet in another sense unique." (175)

We have previously pointed out that Margenau develops observable properties and systems as two kinds of constructs. We have shown that observable properties may be possessed or latent. Observable properties are constructs which lie close to the *P* field but are not elements of the *P* field. Systems are carriers of observable properties.

The simplest and least complicated constructional entity is an external object. External objects, as carriers of observable properties, are examples of a class of constructional entities which Margenau designates as systems. Although he does indicate that in this instance this is a loose use of the term, "any construct which, like an external object, functions in this substantival role as a carrier of observable properties will henceforth be called a system." (172) Some examples of systems are mass points, photons, electrons, electric fields, and gravitational fields. Systems themselves are not measurable, but the properties which characterize them are measurable. Thus, the electron is not measurable, but one may measure its velocity. (176)

In the presence of latent observables, the system, as a carrier of observables, "must be *more* than all the observations performed," since there is no assurance that the observations possess stability. "In the case of atomic particles most observations scatter, and one achieves coherence by pulling them together in common reference to a *system* functioning, as it were, behind them." In the face of a scattering welter of his observations, the physicist chooses the simplest unifying procedure.

He *constructs* electrons, atoms, and so forth, talks about them as systems, and uses them as the carriers of observables. In classical physics, the possessive nature of all properties suggested a carrier so obviously that its specific postulation was almost unnecessary. *In modern quantum theory the carrier thus suggested threatens to dissolve itself and has to be stabilized by a conscious and deliberate methodological act.* (228–229)

But how many properties does an electron or any other system possess? "The fullness of immediate experience leaves their number indefinite; to the probing investigation no limit can be set." Yet a finite number of properties, selected from an infinite number, is sufficient to induce us to apply the term electron to the experience of these properties. A combination of these selected properties allows us to specify the *state* of the electron at a given time. When a certain set of observables is chosen for the purpose of explaining or describing the nature of the system, it is said to define the state of the system. States are special constructs. In the case of a flower, a number of observables, such as shape and composition of petals or the number of stamens and pistils, may combine to form a readily visualized state of the flower. "But when the observables are latent ones, as in the case of the electron, their composition may yield a state which is highly abstract and not representable in visual terms." (173–176)

In these more intricate problems in science, where "intuitive reference is lacking, it is necessary to set down precisely what and how many observables are chosen to define a state." To do this, criteria for sufficiency must be invoked. In particle mechanics, for example, six properties (three coordinates of momentum and three of position) define the state of the system. These six properties are sufficient to define the state as they allow for prediction of the future and past positions of the particle. "By this is meant that *laws* have been discovered which are self-sufficient with respect to states defined in terms of these six quantities." The interplay between laws and states and their mutual dependence is characteristic of science. "States can be defined in a great variety of ways; to be significant, the quantities composing a state must be so chosen that available laws fully mediate between them at different times." Thus Margenau sees discovery in science as "a dual event involving both the selection of crucial variables and the establishment of relations between them." (176–181)

The epistemological process thus described usually starts with the construction of systems which serve as carriers of certain properties. The properties which scientists find fruitful are called *observables*. Two types of observables have been discussed. Some observables may be said to be possessed and some are regarded as latent. A certain set of observables describes the nature of a *system*. This set of observables is said to define the state of that system. The reason that a particular set of observables, and no other, defines the state of the system is that laws have been developed which are self-sufficient with respect to a state defined in terms of this particular set of observables. A more complete discussion of laws is presented within a discussion in Chapter 4.

CIRCUIT OF VERIFICATION

We have previously indicated that constructs may be valid or not valid without discussing the process by which constructs are verified. Margenau refers to this process as the "circuit of verification" or "empirical confirmation."

The circuit of verification passes from perception to the constructional realm where it undergoes a logical transformation and then returns to perception. The logical transformation in the constructional realm permits a return to perception over a different pathway from that which originally led to the formation of the construct. For example, one may "hear the sound from a bell and, remembering simple physics, assume it to be a vibratory disturbance in the surrounding air. Very little reflection then tells us that, if there were no air, the vibrations could not exist and the bell could not be heard." (102) We can now predict that if a bell were placed under a jar and

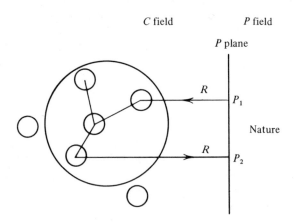

Figure 2. *The circuit of verification.*

Source: Henry Margenau, *The Nature of Physical Reality* (New York: McGraw-Hill Book Company, Inc., 1950), p. 106. Used by permission.

the air evacuated, sound from the ringing bell would slowly die away. This transformation in the constructional sphere marks the return to perception as a nontrivial one.

This methodological movement represents what scientists call prediction. There are two kinds of conditions enabling a prediction: "empirical knowledge symbolized by P_1 [as illustrated in Figure 2] and rational knowledge symbolized by constructs." Predictions are not possible if either of these conditions is missing. (102)

Margenau illustrates the circuit of verification by means of the diagram in Figure 2. In the diagram, P represents "the class of all perceptions that may enter experience. . . . The P field is identical with Nature and might be pictured as a two-dimensional plane, to conform with the lack of analytic depth peculiar to perceptions." The class of all constructs falls within the C field. "The C field is to be thought of as a sort of three-dimensional continuum of rational structure." As the P field and the C field are thus defined by Margenau, he does not mean to imply that a sharp boundary divides these fields, for they are both parts of one continuous experience. (103)

The circuit of verification may function in prediction in two ways. In one way it serves to confirm established theory; in the other way, it serves to establish a new theory. In the first instance, the theory (represented by the large circle in Figure 2) through which the circuit passes must be an accepted theory. In the second instance, the theory is accepted tentatively, and the passage to P_2 is viewed as a challenge to Nature.

If the challenge is met, the theory is said to be confirmed or verified in this instance. And the theory is *valid* if it is confirmed in a sufficient number of instances. Furthermore, the constructs which form organic parts of valid theory will themselves be called valid constructs, or verifacts. *Processes of validation, when conjoined with the metaphysical requirements . . . , create scientific knowledge. It is this purgatory of validation which removes from constructs the figmentary stigma which their epistemological genesis first attached to them.* (105)

Sufficiency

In determining sufficiency, scientists depend upon the orderly relations which exist among constructs before they are put to test. A "pervading rational nexus," which includes the "logical coherence of his conceptions" and an "important sense in which a theory is more than a class of sentences it can generate," allow the scientist to decide which experiments are crucial and to accept a theory after it has been subject to a statistically inadequate number of tests. (106–107)

Prediction

Theoretical prediction as described above is always definite, for a "haze of uncertainty" pervades the P field, and only certainties exist · in the C field. As has been shown, prediction functions largely in the C field. The unsolved question of what constitutes agreement between theory and observation must now be considered. Margenau indicates that predictions are rarely achieved by successive approximations; for, if we were to take this position, it would lead to the perplexing problem of "what" we are to say it approximates. Rather, scientific prediction proceeds through the circuit and, from the haziness of P_1, a prediction is made as to P_2. Such a prediction includes a statement of error. When the theory through which prediction proceeds leads to a P_2, which falls outside of the admissible error, science "looks for new ideas, tries to remember effects it had not included, and predicts again, never sure that the new prediction will be near the old." (116)

The Rational Roots of the Scientific Process

The scientist proceeding under the methodological approach described by Margenau makes sense when he uses measures of precision, when he assigns errors to his observations, and when he discriminates between reliable and unreliable data. In these procedures "lie the rational roots which provide a stable anchorage for his methods and a justification for his use of norms." (115)

True Value

Observation delivers no true value to the scientist. What is taken as the true value for the basis of a given set of measures is fixed by methodological agreement, by more or less arbitrary rules not immediately presented in Nature. Thus,

regulatory devices of the C field must be invoked [at the very boundary of the immediately given] to stabilize the epistemological situation. What is actually done is this: One chooses as the true value of a set of observations the *most probable value* . . . and this happens to be the arithmetic mean.

While Margenau indicates that there is no final agreement among scientists as to the best measures of uncertainty, he does indicate that the probable value, or arithmetic mean, is the most preferred value. (111–113)

Measurement

As the foregoing well indicates, the scientists' concern with prediction leads naturally to a consideration of measurement; for "science in its more advanced stages is interested primarily in experiences . . . called measurement." This interest does not bar scientists from making many observations which do not yield numbers. However, the appeal to number always involves a passage to the C field; it is already a paraphrase of immediate experience. (107–108)

Error

In dealing with measures of uncertainty scientists, have accustomed themselves to distinguish between determinate, or systematic, errors and random errors. Systematic errors are induced by the observer, instrumentation, etc. Random errors are indeterminate in the sense that they have many causes. These random errors are assumed to distribute by the Gaussian curve, and three types of measurement are used in ascertaining them: probable error, standard deviation, and average error. As has been indicated, the preference of physical scientists is for the probable error calculation. (111–112)

Since probable error involves the assumptions underlying distribution by the Gaussian curve, it is well to look at the way in which Margenau discusses aspects of this formulation. He indicates that the scientist uses "normal error distribution both as an inductive generalization from experience and as a criterion for the trustworthiness of that experience." As Margenau illustrates, the normal error curve can be proved on the basis of three hypotheses:

1. There is a *very large* number of agencies, or "causes," producing random deviations.
2. Each agency produces a probability distribution of deviations which has both a finite mean and a finite dispersion.
3. The total deviations resulting from the simultaneous action of all agencies is the algebraic sum of all individual deviations. (114–115)

The normal error distribution is also an important aspect of the scientist's use of the Gaussian curve and, as Margenau states, this distribution is established if we assume that the total number of observations yielding the value x equals the total number of observations times the probability. Thus, we discover the calculation upon which admissible error is predicted as we move in the circuit of verification from P_1 to P_2. (115)

Internal and External Convergence

Since the scientist faces uncertainties everywhere on the level of particularized immediacies, he constantly seeks to achieve greater refinement of perception and to reduce uncertainty. When there are varying measurements, there are two ways in which results can be improved. The first way is to take more observations with the same instrument and, thus, by achieving a more and more accurate mean value, the scientist moves in the direction of achieving internal convergence. The second way is to use more refined measuring instruments. Through this method, external "convergence will be said to exist if the limits of error of the finer set of measurements fall within the range of error of the coarser set." (117–118)

According to Margenau, the question of ultimate external convergence is not now amenable to scientific analysis. He does indicate that there seems to be no available way to reduce intrinsic errors

below a minimum which is apparently fixed in the nature of things. Nor is this an accidental occurrence attending the imperfections of the devices used; to assume that it could be otherwise would contradict known laws of nature. We see that *external* convergence fails. Furthermore, the irreducible error may be quite large. (119–120)

Summary

We have traced the circuit of verification from perception, P_1, via rules of correspondence to constructs, C, and back along a different route to perception at P_2. The circuit of verification may serve to confirm established theory or to test tentatively accepted theory. In both instances, the haziness of perception at P_1 leads to error at P_2, which scientists describe by statistical means. Scientific validity is conferred upon constructs by this continual test against immediate experience through which they are transformed into verifacts.

VERIFACTS

While the problem of reality centers in constructs, the elements of reality are the verifacts, or valid constructs. It is well to remember in this discussion that "constructs are not valid because they refer to something real; on the contrary, they denote something real because they have been found valid." (292) The process through which validity is established is the process of empirical confirmation, or the circuit of verification. This very act which establishes the verifact implies the uniformity of its action throughout time, and, once validated, a construct *"must be said to have been real before it was formed."* (294) While it is important to note that the verifacts are the components of physical reality, it is well to recall that they are not all of reality; for reality is more encompassing than those verifacts which form physical reality. In commenting upon the nature of the "real," Margenau states:

to say that objects around us are real is to claim for them the character of verifacts; it is at once the maximum measure of actualness, of authenticity which can be assigned to them. This protocol of reality, thus understood, is the ultimate epistemological commitment. (298)

The importance of the experience of others as a part of physical reality is confirmed in the following statement: "it is . . . clear that other selves, the experiences of others, have the rank of verifacts in my own experience and therefore enjoy a status wholly commensurate with stars and stones and atoms." (305)

Before discussing the elements of physical reality through the examples presented by Margenau in his analysis of theory, it is well to reiterate that certain relations between constructs and regulative principles guiding scientific inquiry are not in themselves verifacts.

Relations between constructs, such as purely logical relations such as . . . equality, being greater than, and so forth, should not be regarded as verifacts themselves. One must conceive of them as being neutral with respect to the question of reality. The same is true of the regulative [metaphysical] principles . . . ; while their bearing upon reality is very important, they do not lay claim to being real themselves. They might be said to act as verifactors rather than verifacts. (304)

The reality, of which verifacts are the elements, is developed jointly through the process of fitting new parts into an already existing structure of ordered conceptions and by the process of empirical validation. The process of empirical validation has been discussed within this chapter; the structure of ordered conceptions, theory, will be discussed in the chapter which follows; for, without this rational context of theory into which constructs may be integrated, there is no surety that the metaphysical requirements are met.

4

ASPECTS OF
PHYSICAL
DESCRIPTION

Our analysis of physical reality in the previous chapter considered scientific processes in rather broad strokes of immediate and rational experience bridged by rules of correspondence.[1] The rational context within which constructs can be fitted with assurance of meeting the metaphysical requirements is termed "theory." This rational context can, in a sense, include "the certain, even if unconscious, associations and expectations we form about simple objects in our daily lives," but not the uncertain conjectures called guesses and hypotheses. In Margenau's view, it is an epistemological error to consider a "complete severance of entities from theories." He sees "a life of reals apart from the life of theories" as impossible for modern physical science. (292–296) This view is in line with his earlier discussion of the spectacle-spectator problem and the nature of the immediately given, when he commented that the given

must be sought *within experience*. It is wholly unwarranted to *start* a theory of knowledge with the ontological premise characterizing the spectator-spectacle distinction. . . . If it turned out that science becomes impossible or difficult, if experience could provide a stable basis for an objective world from within itself by immanent procedures, then we should be forced to undertake the initial metaphysical plunge. But we hope to show this to be unnecessary. (46–47)

[1] Page references throughout this chapter refer to Henry Margenau, *The Nature of Physical Reality: A Philosophy of Modern Physics* (New York: McGraw-Hill Book Company, Inc., 1950). Quoted by permission.

In this statement the mind as a source of the given is repudiated. Margenau also rejects the absolutely permanent as an aspect of the theory of knowledge. He states that:

The cause of many epistemological fiascoes has been the time-rooted tendency to implant into reality a notion of the absolutely permanent. . . . Static reality is the result of most investigations that remain wholly within the precinct of logic and apply logical rules to preformed objects of experience.

Margenau further indicates that such an approach to reality through logic can hardly include "the imperceptible entities of contemporary theory." In this connection, he observes that "science defines a dynamic kind of reality, one that grows and changes as our understanding grows and changes." (288)

THEORIES

When we view reality as something that is constructed, the relationship of this reality to the nature of theory becomes quite evident; for a theory is an interrelated web of constructs used in the circuit of verification. The combination of constructs is achieved by the epistemic and constitutive definitions which span the entire structure of theories. In turn, the metaphysical principles, which pervade all of our theories about the world, also serve to regulate the theories of contemporary physical science.

Elements of Theories

There are three cardinal elements in theories: systems, states, and observables. In addition there is a "fertile maze of minor constructs which supply vitality to the pattern and make each theory into an evolving enterprise." (171)

We have previously discussed Margenau's characterization of systems as constructs which function in a substantival role as a carrier of observable properties. We have also indicated that these observable properties may be either latent or possessed. The importance of systems in contemporary quantum mechanics is particularly important because of the scattering of observations of atomic particles. One achieves coherence by pulling the observables together in common reference to a *system*. In commenting on system and on the research physicist, Margenau states: "The physicist . . . *can* do his work without it. He would make a great sacrifice, however, for aside from incurring a need for stilted language, he would be forced to accept a very elaborate scheme for making sense out of the scattering welter of his observations." (228–229)

Systems are capable only of constitutive definition, represented by the single lines connecting constructs in Figure 1, p. 25. Some of the examples of systems discussed by Margenau are mass points (with the properties of field strength, potential, derivatives of field strength, etc.), electrons (with the properties of mass, charge, size, etc.), and photons (with the properties of energy, momentum, frequency, etc.) (172)

In order to discuss the states of physical systems, it is first necessary to recall the characteristics of observable properties; for an understanding of these elements is essential to a discussion of states. Observable properties—property observables and latent observables—were described as a part of the discussion of constructs. There, observable properties were described as constructs joined to sensation by rules of correspondence. They alone are capable of being measured; they are not systems, because they are not capable of serving as carriers of observable properties; and their values emerge on observation and secure their definite value only by interaction with an observer. (115)

A certain set of observables is chosen to explain or describe the nature of a system. This set is said to define the *state* of the system. Thus a state is a special type of construct. (95) It is always necessary to indicate precisely what observables and how many are chosen to define a state, and criteria for sufficiency must be invoked in reference to observables in order to define a state. In particle physics, for example, six observable properties are necessary for the prediction of the future or past positions of the particle. In this case, knowledge of odor, color, and the coordinates of position and momentum are too much; knowledge of the coordinates of position and momentum are just enough.

The relationships between the states of systems and physical laws, or laws of nature, are critical relationships. The variety of ways in which states can be defined poses formidable problems for the investigator; for the selection of states in relation to physical laws is crucial.

This apparent regressus, this peculiar interdependence which allows no states to be accepted as significant before laws regulating them are known and no laws to be pronounced as valid before states have been defined, makes the start of every science extremely difficult, makes it indeed an act of genius. Were it not for this dilemma, any field of knowledge could be converted into an exact science by accurately defining states. (180)

The methodological resolution of this dilemma of discovery lies in the embedding of states in relationships to be tested within the confines of an already validated theory or in the formulation of a new theory which takes into account previously verified knowledge and new relationships. For it is well to remember that the most salient characteristic of a valid theory is that it allows laws to be deduced. (169)

In discussing the "circuit of verification," we indicated that the combination of constructs and relations utilized in the movement from P_1 to P_2 forms a theory. We further indicated that if the theory through which the circuit passes is already accepted, the circuit functions as a prediction, but the circuit may also serve as a device for establishing a theory. In the later case, the theory is only tentatively accepted as valid, and the movement through the circuit of verification is considered as a challenge to Nature. (105) Margenau says that "theories are constantly proposed as preliminary phenomenological devices in the hope that they will facilitate the discovery of more adequate explanations." The resultant "explanations" may in some cases be said to "describe" but in other cases to "explain." Hence, those theories which "are de facto said to describe" are referred to as phenomenological theories, while those which explain are called causal theories. (167–168)

Types of Theories

Settlement of the question whether science "describes" or "explains" phenomena cannot be complete until we have investigated more intensively what is to be described or explained, but Margenau proposes that "there is no intrinsic difference between scientific description and explanation." (177)

The distinction between those theories which are said to describe and those which are said to explain is not absolute. Rather, theories can be arranged in ascending orders of "whyness," and the sequence from description to explanation can be considered gradual and never-ending. In those problems with a long scientific history—such as gravitation—it appears that different theories have been designed to permit an understanding of the same perceptual experience. The theories of Aristotle, Galileo, Newton, and Einstein "cannot all be correct because they contradict one another in particulars. The best way to state their relative degrees of validity is to say that each of the first three is an approximation to the fourth and that the approximation is improved from stage to stage." Margenau's conception of the nature of physical reality would indicate that Einstein's conception of gravitational force, as connected with the metric of space, will be replaced by new theories; for he closely questions, "why, after all, should scientific truth be a static concept?" (170–171)

From the examples cited and from many others not discussed here, Margenau illustrates the evolution of scientific explanation. A theory which in its initial period of fruitfulness is used to explain phenomena may, in time, lead to new formulations which will replace the earlier theory. The newer theory will provide a more satisfactory explanation—more satisfactory in terms of the metaphysical principles—and the previously held "explanation" will be looked upon as mere description. (168–170)

Summary

We have indicated that the elements of scientific theories are constructs—systems, states, and observable properties.

We have seen that reality is constructed through the process of fitting new constructs into an already existing structure of theory and by submitting them to the test of empirical verification. The final judgment of the quality and ultimate correctness of a theory will be determined by scientists as they look at "its range of application, taking the generality of a theory as a measure not only of its usefulness but its credibility." (90)

DEFINITIONS

Margenau begins his discussion of the role of definition in science by asserting that "there can be no exact sciences at all under the rigid rule of singleness of definition." His discussion of definition is a demonstration that living science "owes its vitality to the fruitful interplay of two different modes of definition, one closely related to theory and law, the other to the rules of correspondence." (221) The rule of singleness will be analyzed before elaborating the two types of definitions.

Margenau finds the rule expressed in two broad views, which he terms View A and View B. Each, in turn, has two major aspects.

View A is expressed either as one standard definition for a particular phenomenon or as a primary definition with derived subsidiary definitions. Adherents of View A find that any particular given definition is the standard one and it should be adhered to.

Certain physical quantities, like length, mass, electric and magnetic field strengths, lend themselves readily to a substantiation of View A and are therefore almost exclusively chosen by its proponents to exemplify it. Length is defined uniquely in terms of congruences between parts of rigid bodies, (relative) mass is defined as a ratio of accelerations, field strength as the force on some unit entity like mass, charge, or unit poles. . . .
The difficulties in this simple procedure cannot be long concealed. Lengths are not always measured by rigid rods but often by means of sonic, radar, and light waves. Masses are usually determined by weighing, followed by an unstated theoretical conversion from weight to mass. Magnetic field strengths are in practice never found by the definition above because of the unavailability of unit magnetic poles. However, no serious objection to the view in question is occasioned by these facts, for it remains possible to say that the original definitions are *primary* and can be shown, by logical transformations and by laws of nature, to be equivalent to the ways in which the physical quantities are empirically determined. (221–222)

The difficulty of this latter approach, in the view of Margenau, is that secondary definitions need laws of nature in order to be established. To use laws of nature to secure needed secondary definitions is to put a "philosophic slant" on science which Margenau wishes to avoid. (240) He finds, also, that View A becomes more hazy in fields where visualization fails—such fields as thermodynamics and quantum mechanics. (222)

View B is expressed in two aspects: the empiricist argument is illustrated in the work of Bridgman and Carnap and in the rationalist argument. Proponents of View B are most likely to be empiricists and, as such, they appeal directly to observation. If the proponent is a rationalist, he gets along without direct appeal to nature and defines in terms of other quantities. Margenau gives much attention to Bridgman and Carnap. After a full description of Carnap's work, he concludes that, while his logic of measurement remains intact as stated in 1926, Carnap's insistence upon analyzing the physical language and little else "honors but restrains physical activity." In contrasting Bridgman and Carnap, Margenau finds that in Bridgman, measurable properties are actively determined by operations performed by an observer; with Carnap it is "nature whose mode of reaction to changing conditions determined measurable properties for the observer." Although View B recognizes the possibility of several definitions, it insists that they be of a certain type. In this way, philosophers seek to achieve a semblance of unity by indicating "that all definitions, despite their dissimilarity in detail, follow a *single type of procedure.*" (221–231) Thus, Margenau finds View B as rigid and inarticulate as the more primitive View A.

Having dismissed as inadequate the *rule of singleness* of definition for modern physical science, Margenau discusses the distinctions between quantitative and qualitative. He finds such distinctions irrelevant for entities which, by their nature, cannot be measured—that is, the large class of systems; for in these cases even the best definitions remain qualitative. In the case of quantities, "a good definition must indeed be quantitative or refer to procedures for measurement." Denotative definitions are intrinsically qualitative and "are never allowed in an exact science except to the extent that language intrudes them unavoidably." Other definitions of quantities which appear qualitative are so because of defects of statement or understanding. (223–225)

Having considered this customary distinction between quantitative and qualitative definitions, we shall consider two types of definition referred to in the opening paragraph of this section—each of which is quantitative—which together span the entire structure of modern physical science. (237)

Epistemic Definitions

An epistemic definition is one which lies closest to the "*P*-plane" of Nature. (See Figure 1, p. 25) It is a rule of correspondence, or a set of rules of correspondence, and it needs reifying correspondences which link immediate sensations with external object. It would seem that epistemic connections must always end with certain observable aspects of experience. Rules of correspondence are accepted when they prove fruitful. When compelling epistemic correlations are established which cannot be tied in with other constructs, the phenomena are said to be unexplained. A special type of epistemic definition is the operational definition which has been extensively discussed by Bridgman. (236–241)

Four examples of epistemic connections would be: that which exists between the construct "tree" and the vision of it, that which exists between a force and an awareness of muscular exertion, that which exists between the weight of an object and a reading on a scale, and that which exists between a wavelength and its discernment on a photographic plate.

Constitutive Definitions

Constitutive definitions provide the coherence by which different instrumental operations (resulting in epistemic definitions) can be certified on their own merits as specifying the same thing. They allow for the development of systems by indicating which properties under which conditions specify a system. (232, 237)

The constitutive definition, characterized as a postulated grouping of constructs, remains wholly within the C field and is empirically not verifiable. (240) "It is true that all formal connections [constitutive correlations] are stable only as long as certain postulates are maintained, that they are in a sense hypothetical judgments." The range of constitutive definitions can be indicated through the following examples: all relations between geometric quantities which are provable on the basis of a set of axioms; relations between a number and its square; in physics and chemistry, every connection between entities derivable from postulates; relations between force and acceleration of a given mass (Newton's law); relations between a point charge and its electromagnetic field (Maxwell's equations); relations between the curvature of space and the quantity of matter in the universe (Einstein's law of general relativity); relations between temperature and the mean kinetic energy of a gas (Gibbs' statistical mechanics); and the relations between the structure of a molecule and its molecular weight. (84)

Interrelationships of Constitutive and Epistemic Definitions

In an incomplete form, an epistemic definition can be interpreted as constitutive, and an incomplete constitutive definition often appears to be epistemic. The facts of a given science emerge from the active interplay of these two modes of definition. (236–240)

The interplay between the two types makes science a going and self-correcting enterprise. Without epistemic definitions science degenerates to speculation; in the absence of constitutive definitions it becomes a sterile record of observational facts and its formulas take on the character of medical formulas. Physical laws may be regarded as mediators between the two types of definition for specific quantities. In the development of a science, the discovery of a law often leads to new constitutive definitions, and, conversely, a new definition of this type may generate a law. (243)

CAUSALITY

Every theory in the sciences contains or generates constructs that can be used to designate the states of physical systems uniquely and completely. When the states are defined in terms of these significant variables only, Margenau indicates that causal relations exist among the constructs. This conception of causality differs from that in classical physics and from views which described causality in less precise ways.

Classical physics dealt with possessed observables which gave consistent values on repeated observation. States were defined in terms of observables possessed by systems which were linked directly to single observations. In these circumstances, if the relations between states were inadvertently transferred across the rules of correspondence into the P-plane, no factual harm was done. "Atomic physics with its latent observables introduced statistical rules of correspondence, and while states are still causally related, a transfer across these more complicated rules cannot be made." In quantum mechanics the rules of correspondence have changed from a single measurement of an observable to aggregates of observables, but the basic mode of description has remained unaltered. (418–420)

Einstein's work with the special and general theories of relativity extended invariance to "transformations in which the observer passes from one system of reference to another." The special theory extended this invariance to inertial systems, and the general theory attempted to "preserve it for all space-time transformations." Thus, Margenau finds that the work of Einstein on the theory of relativity is "in the deepest sense . . . a natural complement of the principle of causality and indeed its ultimate fulfillment." Today, relativity pervades the entire structure of physics and is classified as a part of classical physics. (411)

Causality in Quantum Physics

The decade prior to 1935 was a major turning point in physics, for in this period quantum analysis began to deal with phenomena in which the observations scattered, and order could only be achieved through the development of new rules of correspondence based upon probability analyses. With this change, "Humean causality is quite definitely gone. Single events of great magnitude cannot be said to have the picturesque single-event causes which classical mechanics envisaged." (418, 420)

Margenau credits Kant with the destruction of the epistemological basis of Hume's analysis of causality, and he finds Kant's greatest achievement is the destruction of the "belief that laws of nature directly involve immediate observations. And if this is true, causality reigns in quantum physics as it did in the classical theory of nature." (420)

In describing the events which brought change in the view of causality, Margenau writes:

The causally evolving φ states are not immediately tied to single observations; they refer . . . to aggregates of observations. Classical description had become noncausal because observables, thought to be possessed by physical systems, had been found to be latent and had refused to give consistent values in repeated observations. This necessitated a reformulation of states in terms of probability distributions: rules of correspondence of a hitherto unexpected type had to be introduced *to restore causality*. (418–419)

Thus, while the descriptive process has remained essentially the same in atomic physics as in classical physics, "the rules of correspondence have undergone radical changes." While knowledge of individual observational events cannot be secured from an analysis of states, Margenau finds that "states continue to evolve in causal fashion." In addition to the support of the foregoing argument, Margenau maintains the causal postulate in atomic physics, because *"no deductive theory even before quantum mechanics defined its states in terms of immediate observations."* (419–420)

Characteristics of Causality

Margenau develops a restrictive formulation of the causal principle. This restriction arises from a desire to establish a unique relation that is noncontroversial, which will "make the principle true in scientific instances where it is known to hold." (396) In developing this formulation Margenau first distinguishes between reason and cause and between partial and total causes. We confuse cause and reasons, he says, each of which may be things, events, or stages. However, a partial cause can only be a thing or event, while a total cause is always a stage in a process. (425)

The causal principle requires systems that are finite both in extent and in the number of constituent particles. The availability of such "closed systems" is necessary for the causal principle to be meaningful. Closed systems are idealizations—that toward which "physical procedures *can be made to tend.*" In this sense, Margenau believes that causality implies that there are closed systems. If, within this structure of closed systems, causality is found to hold, then prediction becomes possible. But the causal relationship is fundamental to prediction and cannot be achieved unless systems are so ordered that causality holds. (421) Since there may be no system in reference to which causality may be found to hold, and since systems are idealizations toward which physical features tend, then "while the principle has positive content, it appears . . . in the role of a metaphysical maxim." But the truth of the principle is not obvious, and it may be wrong. It may happen that

no system can be found with reference to which causal analysis can be conducted. . . . Or it might be that a system is patently given but that to define a state in causal fashion is impossible. If and when these results occur, we do not readily abandon causal description; we endeavor to redefine systems and states. (394–399)

Margenau states the formulation of the principle as follows: "the principle of causality asserts the following: Let A and B be complete states of a specified system at time t_1 and t_2, t_1 being earlier than t_2. If A is realized, B will certainly follow." The principle defines a set of relationships which are both unique and invariable. (393)

When a state is followed by another state, as B follows A, then a system has undergone a change of state. "A cause becomes unique when it refers to a stage in a process involving the whole system under consideration. Or . . . it becomes unique when it refers to the entire *state* of a physical *system.*" Thus a partial cause is never unique and a restriction to total causes is essential to maintain causality. "Not only must the complete state be given, but the complete system must be kept intact throughout all causal considerations." For example, "If state B is the solution of a differential equation for which state A furnishes a complete set of initial conditions, the two are connected inflexibly; B is exactly determined by A and A by B." The essence of such a statement as the above for causality is that time is absent as a variable in the differential equation. This leads to the second characteristic of causality: invariance. (393–406)

Margenau states the relation of the two central characteristics of causality in the following statement: "The point is that we have found a way of describing our experience which renders the relation between two states, separated in time, unique (one implies the other) and invariable (the same implication always holds)." (407)

It is the laws of nature, stated as time-free differential equations, which provide the relationship of invariance which is essential to causality. Thus, Margenau concludes that "all branches of science that have reached a satisfactory state of precision espouse causality as a principle of their methodology, indeed they employ it in the form of temporal invariability of laws in which it has been here presented." (405–412) And at another point, he states:

The force of the principle of causality is methodological, arising from our success at analysis; the principle is a lesson drawn from and continually reinjected into constructive scientific procedures. It lifts the regularities expressed by laws of nature upon a plane of higher generality but does not make them more certain or more secure. (407)

PROBABILITY

Margenau distinguishes between probability as used in science and inductive logic, which Carnap, Reichenbach, Hempel, and others have sought to identify with the theory of probability. His exposition illustrates that "what these men do in effect, and do successfully, is to propose a new formal science, the theory of inference; they are not making comments upon what is now conceived as probability in physics and in the exact sciences derived from it." (247)

While affirming that physical science is a deductive discipline, Margenau clarifies the role of inductive inference in the sciences. Inductive inference is used in physics and chemistry, but it does not characterize these disciplines and is most useful in teaching what it is best "in the face of *incomplete* evidence, where exact science fails." (248–250)

Inductive, or correlational, methods are, of course, found to be of value in the exact sciences:

For . . . they are always needed in order to make verdicts of Nature unique and unequivocal, to trim uncouth immediacies before they are allowed to enter the parlor of constructs. And there are many instances in physics where correlational methods have the last word, where the deliverances of Nature never even see the tidy household of constructs.

The exact sciences are, after all, deductive in their major phases, and the correlational sciences, in striving to become exact, implicitly endorse the methodology of the former. . . . The logical movement of every sufficiently developed science is from the general to the particular, from postulates to theories to theorems to specific predictions. (248–249)

Another distinction between induction and deduction can be seen in a comparison of what is meant when one "notes a fact" and "makes a discovery." The former is inductive and the latter, deductive. A critical condition makes this distinction: "a discovery suggests a fairly general postulational proposition which presses for tentative acceptance, while the fact allows mere inductive generalization." (249)

But the suggestion of significance ". . . by discovered facts is not inductive—it is constructive. . . ." And this constructive process gives to material which had a factual genesis an important sense of being true aside from its origin.

Its [a scientific construction's] universal claim is wholly unsupportable on inductive grounds. It can be *disconfirmed* by a single contravening fact, which is not the case for any proper inductive generalization. Its confirmation, on the other hand, is usually conceded on the basis of a limited number of confirming instances. This, too, is out of line with inductive practice. What happens here is evidently this: Because the deductive method is willing to admit the falsity of a tentative theory with the utmost readiness, we accept its truth, and this means its whole truth, on limited evidence. We never quarrel about its having a truth value of 50 or 90 per cent. When need for that decision arises, we reject the theory in favor of another. (249–250)

General Characteristics

The foregoing discussion indicated that Margenau considers the exact sciences as primarily deductive sciences and that the logic of inductive inferences is inadequate to describe such sciences. In use the exact sciences regard probability "not as degrees of confirmation of empirical propositions, but as measurable (and calculable) physical quantities like lengths, energies, and wave-lengths." (250)

Probability cannot be assigned to a truly single event, to a theory, or to an hypothesis. Its measurement, a physical quantity, proceeds in the same manner as other measurement in exact science with the computation of the "true" value of a number of measurements and with the error noted in the way accepted in the sciences, as illustrated in the following statement of the speed of light: 299,776 ± 4 km/sec. (251–252)

To say that probability is a measurable physical quantity requires that it, like every physical quantity, be definable in at least two ways, one constitutive and one epistemic. The two classical definitions which exemplify the way in which probability meets this definitional rule will be discussed in the following paragraphs.

Constitutive Definition

Laplace's definition, often called the *a priori* definition, is the most familiar of the constitutive definitions of probability. It "takes the probability of an event to be the number of favorable cases divided by the total number of 'equipossible' cases." Laplace's rule is used in science "to advantage wherever the events are *numbers.*" The use of this definition is particularly adaptable to the "large field of games, where attention centers upon unambiguous alternatives . . . ," and the area of heredity. Typical examples of the constitutive area of applicability are:

the number of balls of a specified kind to be drawn from a box in a given number of drawings . . . , the number of successes in *n* independent trials of any operation, the number of alpha particles emitted by a source per second, fluctuations in the number of gas molecules in a given volume. (253–257)

This constitutive definition achieves the relating of the probability to other physical quantities.

Epistemic Definition

The *a posteriori,* or frequency, theory of probability—developed by Ellis, Cournot, and others—uses probability as the ratio of the actual number of times the event occurs in a series of tests to the total number of events. The frequency theory can predict probabilities only through inductive generalization, since it is a rule of correspondence of operational procedures for measuring the relative frequency of the occurrence of some type of event.

The probabilities determined by measuring the relative frequency of an event in a series of trials contain errors which are "symptomatic of their kinship with physical quantities of the more orthodox kind." The "true" probability is computed as the mean of the relative frequencies over a number of series.

At this stage of measurement there is no concern with the distribution of frequencies about the mean, nor is there any need for an appeal to higher-order probabilities, probabilities of probabilities, and so forth, to rationalize such undertakings. One merely hopes for agreement with some constructive theory designed to predict the measured frequencies. (252)

Summary

Modern physical science requires both epistemic and constitutive definitions of probability in order "to get something interesting out of the stagnant logical state of affairs." The attempt to reduce one of these definitions to another is "foredoomed to failure" and any equivalences are a matter of "empirical decision." The relation of epistemic and constitutive definitions to the probability calculus points to the essential value of each. (254)

From the frequency definition alone one does not derive the laws of the probability calculus. Frequencies by themselves can never be construed to imply the two basic theorems of the calculus: (1) The probability for the simultaneous occurrence of two independent events is the product of their probabilities; and (2) the probability that either one or the other shall occur is their sum. It was the historic mission of Laplace's theory to establish logically, to prove, these laws and many others derivable from them. If constitutive definitions were absent from this field, the probability theorist would be in the position of the geometer who is equipped with rulers and compasses but is unable to use the theorems of geometry. (265)

Both Laplace's theory and the frequency theory are necessary if probability reasoning is to be scientific. "The first provides a constitutive, the second an epistemic definition, and every application of probabilities to science must involve aspects of both." (266–267)

CERTAINTY AND UNCERTAINTY

The development of quantum mechanics has brought about significant changes in the way in which physicists represent reality. This shift is a consequence of the change in description, or explanation. The uncertainty principle implies that single observations cannot be determinative of the kind of knowledge needed for prediction in quantum mechanics. It "draws its significance from the deepest stratum of quantum mechanics, from the epistemological doctrine which relates the state of atomic systems to an *aggregate* of datal experience and not to a single complex called one measurement." (362–363) A brief statement of uncertainty might be: when a given state is prepared, the distribution of observables will be Gaussian and any specific individual event cannot be predicted.

Examples

Some physicists trace all uncertainties to the act of measurement, but Margenau believes that uncertainty arises from what has been previously called the haziness of the given, or Nature. In individual cases the effect of the principle may take one of several diverse forms:

[1] interaction between the system under observation and the measuring device may render the conclusions to be drawn very inexact; [2] even without measurement, a system may hide its determinant position under the aspect of being a wave; or [3] a process may occur in which a system loses one form of precision while gaining another. (363)

These interactions characterize the latency of observables.

Quantum theory predicts the probability-in-position of a particle prepared to have a given state function. If electrons are fired by an electron gun at a screen, the number of impacts, when plotted, will distribute by the pattern of a Gaussian type distribution. If the position of the electrons as they emerge from the gun is sharp—and this can be achieved—then all the electrons will strike the screen at one point. When such finite effects are achieved with regard to position, then the uncertainty principle states that the spread of momentum will be infinite. The principle does not preclude measurements of both position and momentum, but it does limit the degree of certainty in measurements of these observables. (357–362)

As previously indicated, the uncertainty principle is a consequence of the latent character of the observables in the quantum realm. The agency of measuring devices is not the source of all uncertainties.

It is apparent that the sources of uncertainty are numerous and do not invariably reside within that narrow class of operations called measurements. On the other hand, the effect of measurements upon physical systems is equally difficult to specify in terms of narrow characteristics. (372)

Measurement

The discussion of the uncertainty principle to this point may seem to indicate that measurement has relinquished the significance it had in classical physics. But Margenau makes explicit the importance of measurement by stating that "measurement, which is the scientist's ultimate appeal to Nature . . . cannot change its singular character without altering the whole of science in a manner far more profound than even quantum mechanics has attempted." He also indicates that measurement is the basic thread of continuity from classical through quantum physics. (369)

Measurement involves a physical system (object) upon which an operation is to be performed, an observable whose value is to be determined, an apparatus for performing the operation; it results in a numerical value. If a numerical value is not produced, "what pretended to be a measurement is merely an *operation*." These characteristics of measurement become increasingly important in atomic physics, where the operation may provide the phenomenon by which the latent observable is discovered. (369–371)

In classical physics, the effect of measurement on a system is presumed to be reducible to a negligible magnitude if sufficient care is taken in the measuring operation, but in atomic systems, the effect of measurement cannot be neglected for two unique circumstances: "the smallness of atomic systems and its consequence, the relatively small amount of energy contained in them; . . . the fact that energy is quantized, the quantum being comparable in size with the atomic energies in question." (373)

In such small systems, observables and operations cannot be distinguished, since operations provide the epistemic definitions for the observables. Thus, "operations capable of leading to measurement, while yielding numerical values, also define the construct known as the observable." The effects of measurement in atomic systems vary from slight disturbances to destruction of the system being measured. For example, direct observations of photons require absorption, which destroys the photon as a physical entity. "Atomic physics has joined biology in recognizing that significant experiments may kill the system." By incorporating statistical uncertainty into its very axioms, quantum theory is able to operate with precision in this kind of situation. By avoiding the necessity of dealing with specific instances and basing its precision upon aggregates of data, quantum theory is able to operate in situations which would be disastrous in classical physics. Quantum mechanics deals successfully with two kinds of aggregates. (370–374)

The first is formed from repeated measurements upon the *same* system, always similarly prepared before observation so that it can safely be assumed to be in the same state $\varphi(x)$. The second kind of aggregate consists of a large number of simultaneous observations on a collection of similar systems, all of which are in the same state. (344)

Quantum physics finds it necessary to maintain the time reference to the state at or before measurement, since in the very process of measurement the system undergoes a change in state. (374)

Summary

Thus we find that confirmation in atomic physics arises from a set of measurements "statistically treated to supply one optimum value" which is placed against a theoretical prediction developed prior to testing through the circuit of verification. (371)

PRINCIPLES OF PHYSICS

The similarities with which the exclusion principle and the principle of relativity operate lead Margenau to consider them as principles of physics. As principles they "enact vetoes on a very basic level of physical description." They impose requirements on the manner in which we formulate our experiences.

The exclusion principle plays a role in quantum mechanics very similar to that played by the principle of relativity in classical physics. These principles operate on a methodological plane similar to that of the metaphysical principles previously discussed, but the demands which they impose "are somewhat more specific than those of logical fertility, extensibility, causality, and so forth, and the discovery of both principles is so recent that their complete amalgamation with the more traditional methods of science has perhaps not taken place." On the other hand these principles are "more basic and more general in their application than the special laws of nature which they force into conformity with their demands." (427)

Thus, the exclusion principle and the relativity principle find a position between the metaphysical principles and the special laws of nature in being more specific than the former but less so than the latter.

The Exclusion Principle

Pauli discovered the exclusion principle in 1925 in analyzing the motion of electrons. In its simplest form, the exclusion principle states that *"no two electrons can be in the same state of motion."* Since its discovery, the principle has been found to apply to most known elementary particles, the best known exception being photons.

More formally, the exclusion principle states that *"no two electrons can have the same four quantum numbers n, l, m, and s,"* where n is a measure of the electron's distance from the nucleus; l is a measure of its angular momentum; m is a number serving to fix the orientation of an electron orbit in space; and s is the spin of an electron about its axis. However, it is from the mathematical formulation of the exclusion principle that the more important consequences of the principle are derived. The development of that mathematical statement and the associated mathematical proofs have no place in this paper, but it is necessary to consider the consequences of the mathematical formulation which requires that *"all functions representing states of two electrons must be of the antisymmetric variety."* This formal choice of antisymmetric functions suggests the action of forces which are not of dynamical origin but are directly traceable to the mathematical properties of the antisymmetric functions. (429–434)

We have here derived a most amazing result, namely, that it is impossible for . . . two particles to come together and likewise that they cannot possess the same velocity! . . . They can neither be at the same place nor move with the same velocity since the probability for these conditions vanishes. . . . In a crude manner of speaking, each particle wants to be alone; each runs away when it "smells" the other, and its sense of smell is keener the more nearly its velocity equals the other's. Somehow, this analogy with sentient behavior seems more appropriate for the description of the correlations here encountered than an appeal to ordinary forces, the chief reason being the very unusual character of the forces, and especially the velocity dependence, which would be required for the purpose. (435–436)

The nature of these new forces is not well understood, but they are not to be confused with ordinary forces.

They are of extraordinary importance and of universal occurrence, providing explanations for all phenomena which arise from the cohabitation of physical particles. Chemical binding, the cohesion of solids, the properties of crystals, magnetism, and many other so-called "co-operative" effects cannot be understood without them. (437)

We previously indicated that the exclusion principle applies to most known elementary particles. The reason for the malfeasance of the photon remains as one of the challenges of modern physics. It is important to indicate "that the principle applies only to particles of the *same kind*. Thus, the states of two protons are antisymmetric, but the states of a system of one proton and one neutron are not." (438, 439)

Relativity Principle

Margenau considers the principle of relativity as a part of classical physics, for it is no longer a subject hidden in a remote niche of physics but pervades and dominates the entire field. The power of the principle lies in Einstein's mathematical formulation, which forces more stringent requirements upon the laws of nature than the temporal invariance of traditional physics. Relativity insists upon "invariance with respect to transformations in which the observer passes from one system of reference to another. The special theory of relativity maintains invariance relative to *inertial* systems; the general theory attempts to preserve it for all space-time transformations." (411)

A further extension of the causal implications of relativity is clarified in Margenau's discussion of the way in which relativity *first* "demands that laws of nature which do not conform to its requirement of invariance shall be dismissed from consideration," (427) *second* restricts causality "to certain classes of events . . . [in which] causal connection extends only to events which lie within each other's light cones," and *third* assigns "all states to which causal evolution may never carry a system . . . to some other causal pattern." (440)

The principle of relativity explains gravitation through physically perceptible forces in the metric of space that do not include the ordinary concept of force. "In the theory of relativity, the important postulate is one which requires that the laws of nature (not the metric!) shall have a particularly simple form." (142) Thus one may observe with relativity, as with exclusion, the unique way in which the choice of the special mathematical statement of these principles forces the laws of nature into accordance with their demands. (427)

The implications of relativity for a changed view of the physical world can be seen in the changed view of simultaneity.

Before the special theory of relativity was known, two events were either simultaneous or not. We have now learned that many conceivable events are neither, or both; two occurrences for example, one taking place on earth and one on the sun, with a time interval of less than seven minutes between them, can also be said to be simultaneous because it is possible to find a system of reference in which both occur at the same time. (21)

It may also be seen in the way in which the superseding of the special by the general theory of relativity changed our physical view of gravitation.

The former found it necessary to adopt the special notion of Newtonian forces, although it treated them in a distinctive and a more successful way. Its virtues were most evident where it confined itself to inertial systems. This led to the distinction between two kinds of forces: those caused by physical agencies (*e.g.*, gravitation, which is due to the attracting earth) and those caused by mere motion of the body under consideration (*e.g.*, centripetal force). Aside from this, the success of the special theory as an explanatory scheme was satisfactory. Then Einstein showed, by generalizing the axioms of geometry, how all forces could be regarded as being of the latter type. Gravitation, which previously enjoyed a status of its own, now appeared as an instance of a more extensible construct: the curvature of space-time. (91)

In the foregoing examples, one can clearly see the way in which relativity has served to reshape men's view of the physical world and in the latter example the way in which the metaphysical principle of extensibility of constructs serves as a director of inquiry just as the principle of relativity forces the laws of nature into conformity with the requirement of invariance.

Summary

The exclusion principle and the principle of relativity resemble each other by imposing formal requirements upon the manner in which we formulate our experience. Both produce correlations which are tantamount to forces but which are not reducible to forces of the usual kind. The parallelism between the two principles has been shown in the remarkable emergence of nondynamic forces. (436–446) it has been said that the relegation of forces to geometry is the greatest achievement of relativity theory. No such discernment has accompanied the discovery of the exclusion principle, which has in fact been even more successful than relativity in extracting physical forces from mathematical symmetries. Here is a range of problems that abound with stimuli for philosophic reflection. (437)

5

THE CONSTRUC-
TIONIST NATURE
OF PHYSICAL
REALITY

Margenau finds a tendency in the sciences to become increasingly theoretical, or deductive, and increasingly less correlational. In making this broad description of tendency, he notes that this is a question of predominance and not exclusion; for all the sciences retain strong aspects of the correlational, or inductive, approaches. His concern is with developing a theory of knowledge compatible with the structure of modern physical science, and he begins by rejecting the ontological premise of a life of reals apart from experience. The nature of physical reality was sought within experience and began with an analysis of experience.

The necessity of formulating a new analysis of physical reality—an analysis described in his book—arose primarily from the inadequacies of mechanism in dealing with quantum mechanics. The use of models, which scientists already had begun to dispense with, proved ineffective in quantum mechanics where the spectator-spectacle dichotomy had dissolved; for in this field the spectator became involved in and modified the spectacle; the knowing and the known became inextricably interwoven. The challenges to physical science presented by the findings of quantum analysis lead to a reformulation of physical theories. This reformulation is what Margenau discusses.

EXPERIENCE AND REALITY

In Margenau's analysis, two aspects of experience are cited as important for physical reality. These aspects are data and constructs—the immediate and the rational. The spontaneity and ephemeral nature of sensory impressions makes them unsuitable as a basis for developing the physically real. On the other hand, the constructional realm is too subjective for physical reality until selective processes can be applied to constructs.

The validation of constructs involves a threefold process, which, for purposes of explication, will be presented in a linear order. First, constructs must undergo the imposition of the metaphysical requirements: logical fertility, multiple connections, causality, simplicity and elegance, permanence and stability, and extensibility. Second, constructs must successfully complete the circuit of verification. The circuit begins at the P plane and proceeds by rules of correspondence to the constructional realm and then returns to the P plane by a different pathway. Third, verification also consists of the establishment of rules of correspondence—epistemic definitions—which link data to constructs as a part of the circuit of verification. Among the more common rules of correspondence are the rules of reification, Bridgman's operational definitions, the assignment of qualities not read from data, the sensory representation—for example, graphing—of phenomena which cannot be seen, construction from mathematical and instrumental processes of such a latent force as field strength, and the assertion of entities from a given complex of data—for example, the electron.

In order to be finally affirmed as valid, constructs—or, verifacts—must be suitably linked to Nature in the ways just described, linked to other constructs by constitutive definitions, embedded in an already established theory, and must be validated by passing through the circuit of verification. Verifacts, verified constructs, are the elements of physical reality, although they are not all of physical reality. Three kinds of verifacts may be recognized—systems, observables, and states. With the developments in quantum theory, observables have become latent; they result from the interaction of the operational processes of observation with the observed. The states of physical systems are composites of latent observables loosely coupled to nature by rules of correspondence of a statistical sort.

ROLE OF THEORY

Theory plays a key role in the nature of physical reality. Theories are constantly proposed as preliminary phenomenological devices in the hope that they will facilitate the discovery of more adequate explanations. In an important sense, theories are more than the class of sentences which they can generate, and scientists are inclined to unhesitatingly accept a theory after it has been the subject of a statistically inadequate number of tests. "To the nonscientist, verification is likely to mean a look-and-see procedure, an artless comparison of what is *predicted* with what *is*." Margenau's analysis shows

how naive it is to suppose that a bare datum of immediate experience invariably carries theoretical significance. On the contrary, it is the formal structure of science that confers relevance on observations; theory determines to a large extent in what manner it will expose itself to test. Historically, therefore, the technique of verification, which is rarely present before a theory is born, developed along with scientific theory and attained refinement in the same measure as the theory did. (446–447)

Verifacts are linked to sense data by epistemic definitions and to each other by constitutive definitions. When a sufficient number of equivalences between constitutive and epistemic propositions concerning a set of physical quantities (states of a system) is established, we have a physical theory and the equivalences take on the character of laws. The criterion of sufficiency places severe intellectual demands upon the investigator; for the interrelated web of equivalencies and correspondences must "fit" simultaneously into a particular kind of coherent pattern. Discovery in science may thus be viewed as a dual event. First, the selection of observables—states defined in terms of specifiable quantities. Second, the establishment of relations—the quantities composing the states must be so chosen that available laws fully mediate between them at different times. Establishing a theory involves a tentative acceptance, and those theories which possess the rationality and coherence imposed by the metaphysical requirements attain validity through empirical confirmation. This continual test against immediate experience enables a physical theory to define its constructs sharply and predict with exactness.

Margenau finds that a distinction between theories which describe and those which explain is not particularly useful, for, in the course of the development of science, theories which were once considered explanatory may now be considered descriptive. Correlational sciences are descriptive, and the exact sciences are characterized by deductive theories which are said to explain. However, the exact sciences also contain theories which describe rather than explain. This distinction between description and explanation—between the how and the why—was seen by Margenau to be primarily a logical one. In the theory of knowledge, the distinction between description and

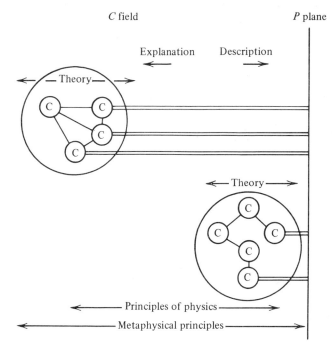

Figure 3. *A simplified schema of the relationships among theories, constructs, epistemic and constitutive definitions, and descriptive and explanatory theories. It also incorporates Margenau's placement of the principles of physics, showing them to have a wider range of influence than theory. The metaphysical principles apply throughout the entire explanatory scheme.*

Source: Adapted from Henry Margenau, *The Nature of Physical Reality* (New York: McGraw-Hill Book Company, Inc., 1950), p. 85. Used by permission.

explanation is dealt with by drawing attention to the "distance" of constructs from the P plane rather than by dichotomizing scientific explanations. Descriptive theories reside closer to the P field and are related to Nature by obvious rules of correspondence, while explanatory theories involve progression into the C field. Thus, we explain by going beyond the phenomena and, in this view, explanation can never be final (Fig. 3).

Through the processes which Margenau describes, modern physical science has developed *theories* that provide criteria for the rejection of illusory data. In presenting this analysis, he rejects a formulation of physical reality that projects a single phase of experience beyond the confines of experience and which, in doing so,

relinquishes control over reality to agencies of doubtful competence; and leaves science without defense against fairies, ghosts, and goblins. For as we have tried to show, unless it be found in the counterplay of construction and verification, there is no available criterion to give reality its warrant and to set it apart from the unreal. (457)

PART 3
FIVE ADDITIONAL
VIEWS OF THE
NATURE OF
SCIENTIFIC
KNOWLEDGE

Certain commonalities with the thought of Henry Margenau emerge as one studies the five works presented in summary form in this part. The works of Bridgman and Frank fall, implicitly at least, within the general contours of Margenau's exposition of the model of the exact sciences. Behind the thinking of each of the biologists—Woodger, Beckner, and Gerard—elements of the same model can be seen. The degrees by which this model is approached as a model for the biological sciences are most clearly evident in the divergent expressions of the participants in the Lee Conference on the "Concepts of Biology." While each of the five authors uses somewhat different terms and different structures for conveying his thoughts, the general framework of a structure of science conceived as having inductive-deductive phases of inquiry which are inextricably interwoven becomes apparent in each work.

The great use of correlational, as contrasted with exact, procedures in the biological sciences is sufficient to raise serious questions regarding curriculum construction and sequencing which enables a student to complete his general education after studying only the biological or the physical sciences.

6

FRANK'S

PHILOSOPHY

OF SCIENCE

The central theme developed by Philipp Frank is aptly put in the title of his book, *Philosophy of Science: The Link between Philosophy and Science.*[1] By using the metaphor of a chain, he describes the nature and function of a philosophy of science in developing an understanding of the strategy and tactics of science. The chain, prior to 1600, was one he found to be continuous, linking science and philosophy at its two termini. (10) After 1600, the chain was split, because science found it more practical to derive the laws from the principles of intermediate generality rather than from the intelligible principles that had directed scientific thought from the time of Aristotle. At about the same time, science and technology began to function as one, and philosophy was no longer the source of verification of principles; if the formulations were practical—were useful in formulating the laws in a simple way—then they were satisfactory, it was no longer needed that they also be "intelligible." (95)

SCIENCE AND COMMON SENSE

Frank argues that this practical view was satisfactory for many of the everyday affairs of science and technology; however, it was not sufficient for the acceptance of theories of high generality. In those

---

[1] Page references in this chapter refer to Philipp Frank, *Philosophy of Science, the Link between Science and Philosophy* (Englewood Cliffs, New Jersey: Prentice-Hall, Inc). Quoted by permission.

instances in which the world view may be altered significantly—that is, geocentric and heliocentric theories, relativity, Newtonian mechanics, etc.—other criteria for acceptance come into play. There are considerations of sociological and psychological import—or what C. S. Pierce has called the pragmatic components of science. (348–354)

The emphasis which Frank places throughout his discussion of the role of philosophy of science in the education of scientists is made particularly clear as he defines the specific role of this discipline. The task of the philosophy of science is to bridge the rupture of the chain and to demonstrate how one gets from the common sense (or "intelligible") view of phenomena to the general principles of science. In his view, it is only through the type of analysis provided in this discipline that one can come to understand what Conant has called the "tactics and strategy" of science. Philosophy of science is responsible for constructing a unified world view within which science, philosophy, and the humanities all have their appropriate relationships. (xv–xxi)

The rupture that occurred as science and technology joined together about 1600, when scientists found it practical to derive their laws from principles of intermediate generality, created other problems than the splitting off of philosophy from science.

The rupture might be said to have had three primary characteristics: the joining of science and technology, the derivation of laws of science from the principles of intermediate generality rather than from the intelligible principles, and the substitution of "ultimate" truth (which the intelligible principles reflected) for "practical" truth (Does it explain the necessary phenomena?) as the criterion for verification of the truth value of a given explanatory scheme. Each of these three characteristics can be seen as a facet of each of the others; thus a new approach to knowledge was developed and the rupture of the chain accomplished. (28–32)

The consequences of the rupture, as discussed by Frank, were profound. The separation of philosophy from science was in time to create scientists who were, in the words of Ortega y Gasset, "learned ignoramuses"—individuals in command of limited technical knowledge and competence but unaware of the meanings of their work for the larger society. Some scientists were unable to distinguish the metaphysical from the scientific aspects of theory, such individuals as those who could see indeterminancy as a scientific provision for free will. Unable to relate the two ends of the science-philosophy chain into a meaningful continuum, some scientists became philosophically the captives of the philosophy they "imbibed" in childhood. (xix)

The rupture also had serious consequences for science teaching—
consequences resulting from the inadequate understanding of the
nature of science and the philosophy of science on the part of scientists, teachers of science, and educators. Textbooks present the
"facts," "laws," or "principles" of science without the underlying
assumptions, as though they are self-evident; organismic interpretations continue; the practical importance of formal systems as contrasted with the description of observed facts is inadequately presented, if presented at all; operational definitions and physical systems
of reference are rarely developed; (98–105) the analogical, as contrasted with scientific explanation, is not clarified; and the "results"
and "facts" are presented without sufficient discussion of the sense in
which "those results are 'valid' or 'reliable' and can be used as a basis
of judgement." (xxi)

Not only have the textbooks suffered from this rupture; the methods of teaching have also been inadequate. Many teachers of physics,
for example, are not able to give their students "a precise account of
the philosophical repercussions of relativity" and, thus, they do "not
fulfill the duties of a physics teacher in a democratic society." (75)
Frank finds that "the dodging of philosophical issues has very frequently made science graduates captives of obsolete philosophies."
The specialization, routinization, and emphasis on an incorrect account of scientific method is pointed out by Frank in a quotation from
Ortega y Gasset's *The Revolt of the Masses:*

A fair amount of things that have to be done in physics or biology is
mechanical work of the kind which can be done by anyone, or almost
anyone. For the purpose of innumerable investigations it is possible to
divide science into small sections and to enclose oneself into one of them
and to leave out of consideration all the rest. . . . In order to obtain quite
abundant results it is not even necessary to have rigorous notions of their
meaning and foundation. (xvi–xviii)

Frank says of the above quote:

The passage quoted from Ortega y Gasset certainly does not describe
the scientific work of men like Newton or Darwin or, for that matter, of
Einstein or Bohr, but it characterizes fairly well the way in which the
"scientific method" is described in textbooks and classrooms where an
attempt is made to "purge science of philosophy" and where a certain
routine type of science teaching has been established. (xvi)

Thus we see that not only the world view of man has encompassed
inadequacies due to the rupture of the chain, but, also, this world view

has brought comparable inadequacies into the ways of thought of the scientist and the ways of teaching science.

THE NATURE OF MODERN SCIENCE

The goal of contemporary science has been to build up a simple system of principles from which observed facts can be mathematically derived.

The procedure of modern science combines the methods of strict logical conclusions with the method of sense observation by confining the logical deductions within a formal system (axioms and theorems) and producing the object of sense observations by applying operational definitions to this formal system. (107)

Thus science works in two levels, the level of sense observation and the level of description by conceptual (verbal) schemes. The level of sense observation can be shared by all, but the conceptual level makes use of language that is many times remote from common experience. "In the evolution of science, the discrepancy between these two levels has increased continually and has become very conspicuous in the realm of atomic objects, such as electrons, nuclei, and the like." (219)

Induction and Deduction

The procedures of contemporary science use inductive and deductive processes in an overlapping, integral relationship. Frank indicates that the formal system develops inductively from sense observation and by human imagination. Induction and deduction are clearly distinguished and at the same time are part of a continuous process of scientific explanation. While Frank uses the metaphor of a chain in his discussion of the movement from direct observation and common sense to the general principles of science, the metaphor which emerges from his discussion is one in which the processes of induction and deduction meet and the chain becomes a circle; but the circle is not alone a linking from deduction of the same observations with which the inductive process commenced, because the deductive process, to be fruitful, must culminate in the prediction of a large number of apparently unconnected facts. This is the same criterion as the "non-trivial" return to Nature discussed by Henry Margenau. (317)

The inductive process begins with observed facts which have been derived from previous deductions and includes new phenomena not previously recorded or noted. From these observations logical, mathematical, and intuitive conclusions are drawn. In time, a conceptual scheme is developed. When the conceptual scheme is sufficiently developed that it becomes a "system of propositions," the term theory is then applied to the scheme. Theories may be general, such as Einstein's, or specific as those of Lorentz and Maxwell. Theory embraces general principles which are symbols connected by logical operations. The form of the principles includes words and mathematical formulas, and it is organized according to the patterns of deductive logic and the rules of syntax. (301–349) For the principles to be of interest to science, they must be stated within a system of reference. From the principles, the values of the state variables of the system may be derived. The laws, or the principles of intermediate generality, are derived from the general principles and are valid if we can describe the state of the system. The laws deal with incomplete cycles. The recurrence of state is defined by a small number of variables, and, as Frank indicates, it is not easy to distinguish between the definition of a law and a return of a state. When operational definitions are developed for the terms of a principle, a physical hypothesis about observed facts is stated, and the prediction of a great number of apparently disconnected facts should be capable of achievement. (283–317) Thus, we see in this description the movement from observed facts to predicted observables as shown schematically in Figure 4.

Verification, Confirmation, and Validity

Modern science prefers verification of phenomena which can be experienced as sense data. Such data are preferred since everyone who has had sufficient training can both comprehend and check them. (299)

Confirmation of the principles of physics is achieved when the observations resulting from experimentation are in agreement with those predicted. Prior to being put to the test of experimental confirmation, the structure of ideas—principles, laws, physical hypotheses, etc.—has to meet the test of logical consistency. (133) With respect to theory, since not all deductive conclusions can be checked, it is generally accepted by scientists that "the theory is acceptable if no

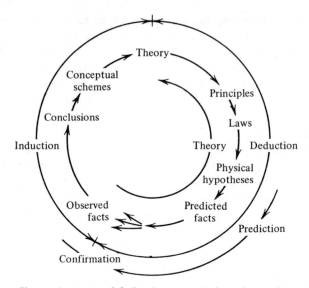

Figure 4. *A simplified schemata of the relationships of induction and deduction to observations, theories, principles, laws, and predictions as interpreted by the writer.*

conclusion is in disagreement with experiment, provided the number of tests is sufficiently great." (349–350)

The validation of a theory in physical science is generally accepted by scientists if it meets the criterion of logical consistency and agrees with the observed facts.

However, if we have to do with theories of very high generality, we notice that they are not uniquely determined by these criteria [semantical and logical]. We also have to consider the pragmatical component, or, in other words, the impact of psychological and social factors upon the systems of signs which have been built up by the scientist as a part of the physical and psychological world. (349)

The actual acceptance of theories of high generality has always been a compromise between the technological and the sociological value of the theory. (357) Thus, a theory which is considered "valid" at one historical period may be considered "invalid" at another—this difference being due in part to psychological and sociological aspects as well as to changes in what is considered to be agreement with facts.

Components of Science

In the concluding sections of his book, Frank, in summing up his discussion, refers to the "components of science" which were first indicated by C. S. Pierce and later given more precise elaboration by Rudolf Carnap and Charles Morris: the semantical, the logical, and the pragmatic (psychological and sociological). Frank particularly emphasizes the importance of the pragmatic component in the acceptance of theories of high generality. On the other hand, the working scientist is most concerned with the semantical and logical components.

7

BRIDGMAN ON
THE NATURE OF
PHYSICAL
CONCEPTS

In this series of three lectures given at the University of London in 1950, Percy Bridgman[1] attempted to clarify "the operations involved in some of our physical concepts, particularly an analysis of the operations into their instrumental and their 'paper and pencil' and verbal components." In this analysis of operations, the author uses the field concept, the concept of empty space, the concept of energy and entropy, and the nature of light as carriers of his general argument. In elaborating upon the operations involved in the content, definitions, and extensions of these concepts, he traces in considerable detail the way in which verbal demands force the extension of old concepts in an essentially unique manner. These extended concepts then demand new experimental effects, which must be checked with experiments. This tracing is based on the idea that until the operations which were used in applying the concept in concrete situations are specified, we do not know its meaning. This operational aspect of the "meaning" of a concept, while not the only aspect, is accepted on the basis of the experience of physicists; for the "objectivity" of operational specifications emerges from their repeatability and identifiability. (5–8)

---

[1] Page references in this chapter refer to Percy W. Bridgman, *The Nature of Some of Our Physical Concepts* (New York: Philosophical Library, 1952). Quoted by permission.

OPERATIONAL ANALYSIS

Bridgman distinguishes primarily between two kinds of operations important in the formation of concepts in physics and in science in general: instrumental and mental. Instrumental operations are those of the laboratory which, in many cases, are operations of measurement. Mental operations include paper-and-pencil operations—for example, manipulation of symbols—and verbal operations. By including mental operations, Bridgman refutes the mistaken idea that "the operations which give meaning to a physical concept *must* be instrumental operations." He gives considerable attention to the fact that "civilised man lives to a large extent in a verbal world of his own making: in this verbal world he exhibits patterns of behaviour which he finds no less compelling than the patterns forced on him by the 'external' objects of the physical world." (8–9) The relationships among the kinds of operations that have been presented are shown in Figure 5.

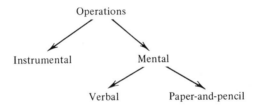

Figure 5. *Kinds of operations.*

Although each of these kinds of operations is important to the structure of science, the lines of separation among the operations are by no means sharp. There are essential interrelationships between mental and instrumental operations; for verbal demands and paper-and-pencil manipulations lead to constructions to which complete instrumental status may eventually be given. Through his discussion of these interrelationships, one may come to see that physics (and Bridgman is concerned with thermodynamics and not theoretical physics) does not allow full freedom to the paper-and-pencil constructions but requires that they shall be capable of verification through experimental arrangements. Such verification does not proceed automatically, however, for the correspondence between the paper-and-pencil and instrumental operations is not unique. There is, in fact, a "hiatus" between the two. To move from data to a smooth curve requires a logical jump, but at the same time it makes generalization possible. Thus, for example, there is no physical operation which corresponds exactly to the mathematical operation of taking the limit. Failure to recognize this lack of unique correspondence may lead and, indeed, has led physicists to reify objects revealed through experimentation and consequently to expect such "objects" to have all of the characteristics of the mental construction. (14–26)

Paper-and-pencil operations, by allowing for greater generality than instrumental operations, suggest experimental possibilities and facilitate instrumental investigations. For example, the construct of physical fluxes was suggested by paper-and-pencil demands and was later discovered through experimentation. (28)

This brief discussion has served to illustrate the essential interrelationships among the various kinds of operations. It also serves to illustrate the problem of discussing the existence of "things," as one does when referring to matter and energy as two "things" composing the universe. In discussing an example of the way in which constraints are imposed by the instrumental verification of physical concepts, Bridgman is led to deny physical content to "empty space."

In this denial of the legitimateness of the concept of empty space it seems to me that we have as dramatic a demonstration as can be imagined of the impossibility of divorcing our concepts from the operations by which they are generated and of the impossibility of speaking of things existing of themselves in their own right. (19)

Not until operations can be so performed that they result in instrumental detections which are both unique and necessary does Bridgman find the processes to have full physical content. "Unique" and "necessary" are not defined explicitly by Bridgman, but their operational meaning would seem to encompass the following aspects: in any instance, physical reality would be expressed in the simplest conventions which will account for experimental observations, fit mathematical and verbal constraints, permit detection, maximize prediction, and be acceptable to common sense. While "uniqueness" allows for the instrumental verification of a construction, the quality of "necessary" means that the unique solution can be fully rationalized through the entire body of the science. A construction achieves physical significance in the meanings discussed by Bridgman only when each aspect inferred by the construction can be found capable of instrumental verification without being separated into its component parts. For example, fluxes must be capable of measurement without being analyzed into thermal and mechanical components, and such a method has not yet been devised. Thus, "the flux of energy situation remains on the formal level, where it serves the function of giving consistency and completeness to our paper-and-pencil treatment." (22–33)

SOME ADDITIONAL ASPECTS OF THE NATURE OF SCIENCE

Although Bridgman does not discuss fully the nature of science in his treatment of the nature of selected physical concepts, he does develop some aspects of science which are important for this discussion. Much of the development of these ideas is embedded in his argument of the relations of operations. The purpose here is to search out these discussions and to focus them upon such ideas as concepts, the use of analogy in science, natural laws, and acceptance and verification.

Concepts

Physical concepts are dynamic; the verbal and paper-and-pencil components of them extend existing concepts in unique ways that force new experimental effects. It is the interaction of the verbal, paper-and-pencil, and instrumental operations which provides for the development of the meaning of a particular concept; for this development is dependent upon the specifying of operations used in applying the concept in concrete situations. Such meanings develop from both instrumental and noninstrumental operations, even though it is through instrumental operations that concepts come to have physical content. "Simple observation shows that physicists do profitably employ concepts the meaning of which is not to be found in the instrumental operations of the laboratory, and which cannot be reduced to such operations without residue." (8) This residue, an element of pure construction, becomes a component of the meaning of the concept. But those concepts not capable of eventual instrumental emergence, which are permanently confined to the verbal domain, remain outside the field of physics. Thus physical concepts need to have both instrumental and mental components or need to be considered capable of eventual instrumental emergence. They are defined by an interlacing web of instrumental and mental operations. In addition, most physical operations enter into some theoretical structure. (9–10)

When rival concepts cannot be instrumentally verified, one may be preferred over the other. For example, neither the concept of light as a "thing traveling" nor of light as a "thing departing and arriving with retardation of time" can be instrumentally verified;

whichever point of view is adopted it must be described as a convention. It may well be, however, that one of the two alternative points of view is so much more congenial to the commonsense way of looking at things, the commonsense point of view itself being recognised as at bottom a construction, that we . . . adopt it in preference to the other. (21–22)

But the preferred concept must meet the constraint of being applicable to all the situations for which it is appropriate, and it must function within the broader framework of the theory of which it is a part. (25)

Analogy and Common Sense

The analogy of a "thing traveling" seems to stimulate experimental verification by treating light through mental experiments and paper-and-pencil operations in much the same way as ordinary macroscopic objects are treated. This mental operation of asking questions by analogy is often fruitful in suggesting new experiments in the instrumental world. Such use of analogy is often constructive, but the danger of reifying the mental operation must not be overlooked; for Bridgman reminds us that we cannot either see or feel a photon in flight. This commonsense way of conceptualizing light introduces the ordinary way of thinking of the objects of daily life, in which objects have an existence independent of the instrument or method used for observation. The selection among alternative points of view on the basis of congeniality with common sense should include an awareness that a particular convention is being adopted; one should not consider that the selection has a logically unique basis. Bridgman urges scientists to recognize that commonsense views color all of their thinking and that when they carry them uncritically into interpretations of physical phenomena, their analogies may be unjustifiably extended. He argues that this role of common sense is not generally accepted in science and, therefore, requires consideration. (16–20)

Natural Laws

The nature of natural laws is most fully discussed by Bridgman in his presentation of the first law of thermodynamics: $dE = dQ + dW$. This method of stating the law indicates that the "universe has been divided into two parts: the 'system,' to which the law as written applies, and the rest of the universe, 'external' to the system." As written, the ostensible meaning of the first law would imply that each component of the equation could be determined by independent instrumental verification in all instances; but this is not true at the present time. However, in those instances where the first law alone is applicable, the terms of the equation are capable of full instrumental verification and the equation is thus termed a "natural law." (23–34)

A natural law, since it is

ostensibly of a complete generality, applies not only to the original system but also to any sub-system which can be carved out of the original system in any way, not only by actual physical division, but in the paper-and-pencil domain by drawing imaginary surfaces in any way in the interior of the original system or even in the space outside it. For any conceivable sub-system, the equation must have meaning." (27)

In his discussion of the first law of thermodynamics, Bridgman traces the development of the equation from its beginning

as a formal equation of definition of dE, and therefore with a strong paper-and-pencil component of significance, . . . [to] an equation in which each term has independent instrumental significance, and therefore as an equation which in any specific situation is capable of complete instrumental verification. As such, it has evolved from a definition to a statement of a "natural law." (34)

Acceptance and Verification

Bridgman gives his greatest attention to the problem of verification, which he relates to his major task of clarifying relations among operations. The most significant aspects of his views regarding the acceptance of competing concepts have been considered, but some additional comments need to be added.

Early in the development of a science there may be little reason to choose between two points of view. The discovery of new experimental facts may provide such convenience and simplicity for one point of view that it will become accepted. This does not imply that such acceptance is merely a convention; for acceptance, a concept must be "unique," must be applicable in all instances where the particular phenomenon is found, and must be capable of being rationalized through the whole discourse of its science. (25)

The operational verification of differential equations is of major concern in Bridgman's discussion of thermodynamics. "We regard the differential equation as verified if we can detect no consistent discrepancy between the smooth curve which we draw so as to satisfy the equation and the plotted experimental points," he says. A law of nature formulated in differential form may thus be directly verified, even though the hiatus between paper-and-pencil and instrumental operations remains. Such procedures of verification come to be accepted over periods of time because of the success of such methods for prediction. In this regard, Bridgman indicates that

many of the contemporaries of Newton or Leibniz would have keenly felt the need of an experimental verification of the possibility of representing any actual situation by a differential equation. For the concepts for dealing with motion are not easily derived from the concepts with which static situations may be successfully handled, nor is the concept of a mathematical limit easy or its connection obvious with what we do in the laboratory. *It must have been many years before our present mental serenity was acquired in the face of the operations of the calculus.* (Italics mine.) (13)

In his discussion of the creation and flow of entropy, Bridgman distinguishes between verification that relates to physical significance, or physical reality, and verification of the correctness of expression. The differential form of the statement of natural laws, in this case the second law of thermodynamics, "has only a verbal and not a physical significance, but there is, nevertheless, a certain compulsion associated with it." (38) The form would be retained regardless of the experimental situation.

Thus, there may be statements of such significance to an explanatory scheme that, even without unique instrumental operations, they would be retained to give coherence to the entire scheme. In the absence of instrumental operations, coherence may be found in the paper-and-pencil domain by connecting with some theory. Paper-and-pencil and instrumental operations thus mutually reinforce and supplement one another. But the quest in the physical sciences, as well as the central arguments of Bridgman's lectures as stated within thermodynamics, is to achieve the unique and necessary instrumental operations essential for prediction. As Bridgman states:

it seems to me that the broadest basis on which we can hope for an eventual understanding is *invariable correlation between the results of instrumental operations.* Given invariable correlation, we can find how to predict, and prediction is perhaps the most searching criterion of understanding. (17–18)

SUMMARY

For those who have read his earlier works, *The Nature of Thermodynamics* and the *Thermodynamics of Electrical Phenomena in Metals,* and built upon them as though the explicitly stated were his only concern, Bridgman provides a caution that other aspects of analysis were embedded in those arguments.

The analysis which I here present of the way in which our verbal demands force these extensions of concepts is a much more self-conscious analysis than I made in the two books in which I first extended the concepts. In the books it merely appeared to me that my argument had a certain inevitability, without much reflection on my part as to how it was that I had a right to argue at all. (6)

In extending the idea of operational analysis to include mental as well as instrumental operations, Bridgman has shown how these operations mutually interact to achieve greater generality. While the impossibility and meaninglessness of separating these two kinds of operations has been developed (61), the analysis of a number of physical concepts increases the reader's awareness of the significant role played by each and is illustrative of Bridgman's increased appreciation "of the importance of the role which our verbal demands play, not only in the structure of our formal theories, but also as a tool capable of supporting new experiments." (5)

8

WOODGER ON
BIOLOGY AND
LANGUAGE

Woodger's work[1] is primarily concerned with methodological problems in the sciences and in biology as a particular science. Although one may think of biology as dealing solely with organisms, Woodger's discussion is centered on the premise that biologists make observations of organisms and produce records—observation records; but when they develop hypotheses and theories, they are no longer speaking about organisms but about statements. This premise leads Woodger to his central concern—an investigation of the language of biology—for he states that "science can only deal with shared thoughts, and thoughts can only be shared effectively by the use of language. When I speak of biology I shall mean the system of accepted written or printed biological statements." (7)

Throughout this work, Woodger seeks to maintain a consistent nominalistic position—a position which maintains that there is an irreducible antithesis between feeling and doing. In developing this position, he rejects the habit followed by many biologists of talking about properties of organisms and chooses to develop his argument in terms of the extensional point of view. Extensional methods enable one to avoid talking about properties by using property words to specify sets. In genetics, for example, speaking of phenotypes is speaking about sets and is therefore extensional, but if biologists

---

[1] References in this chapter refer to Joseph H. Woodger, *Biology and Language, an Introduction to the Methodology of the Biological Sciences Including Medicine* (Cambridge: Cambridge University Press, 1952). Reprinted by permission of the publisher.

make such statements as "the pea-plant *a* is tall," (23–26) it is easy for them to continue with such statements as " 'tallness is handed down from parent to offspring,' which is at best an unfortunate metaphor and at worst a most misleading product of the intensional point of view which has generated enormous confusion during the short history of genetics." (24)

Woodger emphasizes the necessity of developing a critical attitude toward language in science. A good scientific language should be brief and fully generalizable, and it should contain a minimum vocabulary of basic functors. Syntactically, Woodger recognizes two elements in observation records—individual names and functors. Functors name set or class membership rather than properties. A statement "rat *a* is black" asserts that the object, "rat *a*," (individual name) is a member of the set "black" (functor). The case of elliptical language in textbooks and in the technical journals has been a source of misunderstanding and confusion. The uncritical borrowing of terms from the natural languages has also been a source of misunderstanding. In genetics, some examples are the expressions *heredity, inherited character, acquired character, determines*. The magnitude of the problem increases with "the curious but powerful tendency among biologists, when confronted with alternatives, to regard them as mutually exclusive; it has so often been 'heredity *or* environment,' 'nucleus *or* cytoplasm,' but *not* both. (279)

By making use of the thought which has emerged as part of the Boole-Frege movement, Woodger shows that alternatives can be developed to provide a more precise language for science. His examples demonstrate the power of his system in clarifying hypotheses, ordering them into levels, and deriving consequences from them.

LANGUAGE IN SCIENCE

Woodger is primarily concerned with statements about organisms. He maintains that "language is just as indispensable a tool for the pursuit of biology as microscopes, kymographs, and other instruments." The natural language is shown to be inadequate for biology, and he indicates that the most highly developed sciences, physics and chemistry, are the two which use symbolic languages. (5)

Woodger examines four languages of interest to his exploration of selected aspects of genetics, neurology, and medicine. The burden of his argument is that the physical language—the language of chemistry and physics—is insufficient to the expression of relationships which exist in neurology, psychology, and medicine. The use of physical language when dealing with persons leads to a dualism with the alleged entities of "mind" and "body." Restricting the natural sciences to the physical language reduces the problems encountered only if the problems investigated are also reduced. He demonstrates that additional languages eliminate the confusion of physical objects and sensible objects. (255–319)

The activities of biologists include observation, experiment, and the formulation of hypotheses. In order to carry out these activities, the biologist must use language as an important tool. Woodger cites a statement from a report entitled *The Training of a Doctor:* "The student should . . . be disciplined in *the proper use and meaning of words and the relationship of names and words to ideas and things."* He believes, however, that teachers are not properly trained to achieve this goal with their students. (61)

Woodger classifies biological statements into two mutually exclusive categories: observation records and theoretical statements. Observation records are rarely reported in the literature; they sometimes are found in laboratory records and notebooks. Frequently they remain implicit in reported theoretical statements. For example, the record of a specific number of grams of oxygen evolved by an aquatic plant includes some chemical theory and would, therefore, exemplify the simplest kind of theoretical statement. Observation records are made with the help of only as much theory as is inevitable when using commonsense language. They are adopted as basic statements by which all others are tested. All other statements are considered to be theoretical. Biological statements, on the other hand, are in a sense hypothetical, in that they go beyond strict observation. Woodger is concerned with these distinctions in order to avoid the difficulties biologists get into when they make statements about organisms. (31–45)

Woodger shows that the process of induction functions in the deriving of consequences from hypotheses. The use of the consequence relation provides for the ordering of hypotheses in theory building. Deduction finds its place in Woodger's methodology of science in the definability relation. He finds that the distinction between the two processes has been blurred in the writings of biologists.

Although biology, like the other sciences, begins with observations and the communication of them—observation records—Woodger points out that it is primarily through theoretical statements that biologists communicate with one another. Through a discussion of Harvey's studies of blood circulation, and again in a discussion of elementary genetics, Woodger illustrates the development of zero-level hypotheses and explanatory hypotheses of higher levels. The jumps from a few observations to a generalization—from one frog to all frogs—is a seemingly unconscious action. This resulting generalization is termed a zero-level hypothesis, not testable, but usable. Restrictions are imposed on generalizations only when new observations require them. Hypotheses go beyond the strictly observable and must be tested to become a part of a theoretical statement. Theoretical statements are tested by the processes of falsification through which the consequences of hypotheses are tested, until such time as an observation record comes up which contradicts them. Woodger demonstrates that no matter how remote hypotheses are from observation records they remain within the reach of falsification, provided they belong to a sequence of statements which can be subjected to the analytical procedures outlined in the discussion of the processes of falsification. (56–59)

By developing a more precise language and by using this language to reach a generalization of elementary genetics and a classification of genetical systems, Woodger hopes to encourage other biologists "to keep alive the spirit of inquiry and not to allow ourselves to be satisfied with traditional attitudes and traditional language in which so much of traditional belief is embedded." (317)

SCIENTIFIC THEORIES

Woodger uses the term "theory" for systems of theoretical statements ordered by the consequence relation. In a fully axiomatized theory, explanatory hypotheses would be arranged in a pyramidal order in such a way that each member of a given level (omitting the top) is a consequence of at least one member of the level immediately above it. In each higher level within the pyramid of statements, new subject-matter and new terms are introduced, for "one of the purposes of passing to a higher level is to widen the scope of our theory so that it embraces more of the subject-matter of the science to which it belongs." (124)

The invention of hypotheses and their subsequent testing is the first step in theory construction. Observation records do not enter into

Final level of hypothesis is the most concise statement of the theory and is not itself a consequence of a higher level hypothesis.

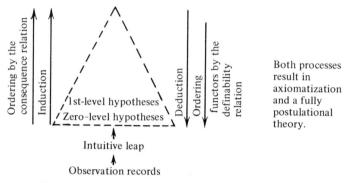

Both processes result in axiomatization and a fully postulational theory.

Figure 6. *A schema representing some aspects of theory building.*

theories, but they are of paramount importance to theories because they are the records by which theoretical statements (hypotheses) are tested. The invention of hypotheses is a major contribution to the growth of knowledge in biology, for such growth does not come by accretion, but rather through frequent readjustment between theory and observation. He cites as an example the invention by Harvey of an hypothesis regarding heart action, with its many consequences for physiology. (4) Hypotheses perform the functions of grouping generalizations into larger and larger groups and in establishing links between groups. In this way, the supporting base of observation records is broadened and further inquiry is stimulated.

Woodger's major contribution to the discussion of a structure of science is his analysis of the way in which observation records and theoretical statements are distinguished—the intuitive leap which is made to zero-level hypotheses, and the pyramiding of hypotheses through the consequence relation into a coherent theory which may, as it becomes a matured theory, have its functors ordered by the definability relation and thus emerge in time as a fully postulational, or deductive, theory. In such a theory, all definitions are either contextual or explicit. Thus, the area of the ostensive definition lies in the early stages of inductive formulation.

9

BECKNER ON *THE BIOLOGICAL WAY OF THOUGHT*

The question of the necessity for a distinctive way of thinking about living organisms, in contrast to the inanimate aspects of nature, is the major concern of Morton Beckner's work.[1] His concern is restricted to those aspects of biological explanation which fall within "organismic biology." At the same time, Beckner indicates that there are phenomena of interest to biologists which are amenable to the methodologies and explanatory schemes exemplified by the physical sciences. With these restrictions, Beckner's work centers on "certain problems of biological theory—the problems of teleology, organization, and historicity—by way of the *actual methods* used in dealing with them." (Italics mine.) (12) The restriction of the analysis to the *actual methods* used by organismic biologists at the time of his writing limits Beckner's exposition to an exploration of these problems from within the organismic frame of reference.

ORGANISMIC BIOLOGY

Beckner proposes to show that the doctrines and methodologies of organismic biology represent "a positive attempt to come to grips with real problems," but he has "tried to be guided by conservative maxims, i.e., to assume, unless contrary evidence proved to be conclusive, that *sui generis* methods are not required in biology." (2, 5)

---

[1] Page references in this chapter refer to Morton Beckner, *The Biological Way of Thought* (New York: Columbia University Press, 1959). Quoted by permission.

Four doctrines of major importance to the organismic perspective in biology are identified: organizing relations, directiveness, historicity, and the autonomy of biological theory. The doctrine of organizing relations argues for a holistic approach to the study of organisms. Levels of organization above the physicochemical are exhibited by organisms and, though the chemical composition of organisms is recognized, "these constituents are organized in such a way that the wholes composed of these constituents exhibit behavior and properties that are not chemical." (5–8)

The problem of directiveness, or goal-directed behavior, has plagued biological explanation for generations. Directiveness may be considered as one aspect of the problem of biological organization; for Beckner includes within this doctrine "the relation between structure and function, goal-directed behavior, and behavior that subserves any of the biological 'ends' of maintenance, reproduction, or development." (6) Concepts formulated for describing the activities of organisms may consider the end served or goal attained. (188–189)

The third doctrine asserts that the "historical character" of organisms produces special methodological problems for biological theory. Five major "facts" are assembled to support this doctrine:

(a) All organic systems have histories, and part of the duty of the biologist is to give a descriptive account of these histories; e.g., paleontology describes the successive changes in forms of groups of organisms, and embryology describes the normal changes that characterize the histories of individual organisms. (b) The past of an organic system determines, or helps to determine, its present structure and behavior. (c) Many types of organic change, e.g., ontogeny, regeneration, and evolution, are serial or irreversible. (d) Many organic changes are properly described by the term "development." "Development" includes growth, elaboration, and differentiation, accompanied by the appearance of new potentialities, at a higher level of organization. This occurs in both ontogeny and phylogeny. (e) Finally, the course of development from germ to adult organism is determined in part by the past history of the ancestors of the organism. (6–7)

The logical problems of explanation raised by these assumptions become a central concern in Beckner's work.

The three doctrines described led Beckner to propose a fourth doctrine—partly descriptive and partly prescriptive. This doctrine asserts that the organism should be examined "without prejudice, preconception, or unconscious bias, in order to discover and relate the properties it has *qua* living organism." This doctrine further holds that concepts not definable in physicochemical terms are appropriate for biology. The fact of biological organization thus makes legitimate and profitable use of "specifically biological" concepts and laws. (8) Beckner supports this doctrine

not because these properties are unparalleled in the organic world, or in some sense are "irreducible" to inorganic properties, but because the systems which possess them do in fact exhibit relations with each other and relations among their parts that may be explained while abstracting from, or, more accurately, simply ignoring the underlying physicochemical mechanisms. (9)

His argument does not claim that such description of phenomena is the only one which may be used. By describing phenomena exhibited by organic parts in explicit relation to the phenomena exhibited by the wholes of which they are part, organismic biologists claim greater success in the yield of generalization than in alternative descriptions.

It is important to note that Beckner concludes, after extensive examination of biological systematics, selection theory, and other higher-level areas of biological concern, that organismic biologists do not claim that the properties of a part of a system are determined by those of the whole system nor that phenomena at a lower level of organization may be explained by reference to phenomena exhibited at a higher level of organization. Rather, Beckner would formulate their position by stating that "The concept of the whole determines the concept of the part." (187–188)

The substance of *The Biological Way of Thought* centers on an examination of the concepts employed by organismic biologists, and in genetic and teleological explanations which organismic biologists employ in dealing with teleology, historicity, and organization.

BIOLOGICAL CONCEPTS

Three classes of distinctively biological concepts are considered characteristic of biological theory—The "polytypic," the "historical," and the "functional." They play a large role in biology (and also in other sciences containing a large measure of natural history), in that

their utility in biological theory is derived from exactly those features of biological subject-matter that raise the interesting questions of biological methodology, namely, the great complexity, the historical character, and the organization of biological systems. (22)

These three classes of concepts are characterized by distinct modes of definition or relationships between the definition of the concept and the operations that warrant the application of the concept. Well-defined (W-defined) concepts are distinguished from effectively defined (E-defined) concepts on these bases: W-defined concepts are intended to be an application of the verifiability criterion by providing both necessary and sufficient conditions. W-defined biological concepts would permit the formulation of E-definitions which could become statements of explanation according to the Humean Pattern. (88) However, Beckner provides for the formulation of E-definitions which possess certain "W-defining criteria of adequacy." (17–21) In this way, E-defined concepts, such as "presumptive neural plate" in embryology, are provided for. His finding that many biological concepts provide for sufficient, but not necessary, conditions becomes part of Beckner's argument for uniquely biological types of concepts.

Polytypic concepts are numerous in biology, especially in systematics. Polytypic concepts are defined by reference to a set of properties such that each individual in the class possesses a large number of properties, each property is possessed by a large number of individuals, and no property is possessed by every individual. The species category and the taxa of higher rank in taxonomy are polytypic concepts in that members have a "family resemblance." (22–23)

Historical concepts are those in which a process describable as a temporal sequence is always involved. "Hybrid," "mutant," and "backcross" are examples of historical concepts from genetics. (25–26)

Functional concepts incorporate implicit or explicit processes. When the classes of systems or processes are defined as the extensions of functional concepts, they are said to "contribute" to the "function." Most organs, such as "kidney," as well as the terms "releaser," "danger signal," and "symbiote," are offered as examples of functional concepts. (27–28)

The foregoing discussion is not intended to imply that the three classes of concepts are mutually exclusive classes. The polytypic E-definition is utilized in the application of both historical and functional concepts; and in Beckner's discussion of systematics, genetic analysis, and teleological explanation, he provides further examples.

These concepts have a logical feature which distinguishes them from concepts typical of the physical sciences, in that

in order to apply them truly to any system S, certain facts must be true about systems other than S: some of the properties of S must be widely distributed in a class of systems that may bear absolutely no relevant causal relation to S; or certain events, the "P-events," must have occurred in the past; or S must contribute to a function F' of a distinct system S' when S' is in some environment. (28–29)

The above definitions of classes of concepts leave the borderline between class membership and nonclass membership indeterminate and, thus, they serve when theory is lacking. They "provide the biologist with a 'key position' for the analysis of phenomena that depend upon the organization of physical, chemical, or higher level parts, without taking explicit account of the parts, their organizing relations, and the laws that describe their interactions." (31) Such concepts, however, are not admissible into fully systematic and well-formalized theories such as occur in the physical sciences—for example, Newtonian mechanics. (184–185)

BIOLOGICAL EXPLANATION

In considering the nature of explanation as developed by organismic biologists, Beckner refers again to the problems of teleology, historicity, and organization. He finds that models serve a number of logical roles in the explanatory systems in all three areas. In the area of historicity, he distinguishes two logically distinct patterns of explanation designated as genetic analysis and genetic explanation, rejecting the term "historical." Two patterns of teleological explanation are distinguished: functional analysis and teleological explanation proper. (81)

Models are considered to yield explanations and to serve most of the functions of theories rather than having a purely heuristic function. When models are coupled with genetic analyses or with functional analyses, they yield genetic or teleological explanations which are widely utilized by biologists. Models in which the explanans may be known to be false, or certainly not known to be true, present quasi-explanations of events at one level of organization in terms of parts of a lower microscopic level. These models are further characterized by two kinds of simplifying assumptions. First, law-like statements about the elements of the subject, which simplify because they serve to reduce the structural complexity of the field, may be introduced. An example of such a statement is the model-explanation of dark and light eye color in man in terms of a single pair of alleles. This type of model, when coupled with a genetic, teleological, or functional analysis, produces a genetic, teleological, or functional explanation. Second, subsidiary hypotheses may be introduced to simplify by idealization, restriction of the scope of the model, etc. For example, in certain genetics models, linkage or crossing over is sometimes neglected. Such hypotheses refute the view of models as analogies, for the known properties of the model's subject and the nature of the phenomena to be explained control the kind of hypotheses which may be introduced. (38–54)

Beckner considers phylogenetic explanation as a form of genetic explanation, since it serves to explain phenomena which appear to be the outcome of a temporal sequence of events. Teleological explanation plays a role in explaining directive activity and goal-directed behavior. While philosophers see no particular relation between goals and purpose-like actions, Beckner maintains "that the goal 'determines' the prior activity in the sense that knowledge of the goal is a necessary precondition of Humean explanation of the goal-seeking activity." (149) Teleological explanations are useful in considering goal-directed behavior, such as when a fish swims into a hole in a reef when attacked. Such explanations become useful when interest centers on the relation of feedback variables to environmental variables and when the state of knowledge of a larger system of which the teleological is a part is not adequate for developing nonteleological explanations. (148–154)

Beckner states that among the biological sciences only in genetics has a highly articulated deductive system capable of axiomatic treatment been developed. The theory of evolution is an example of a particularly biological theory of interest, because of its success "in integrating into a single body of theory the results and data from the most diverse branches of biology; paleontology, genetics, ethology, systematics, biogeography, ecology, etc." (159) The term theory in this case is not used to indicate an articulated deductive system, but a "family of related models that explain or quasi-explain empirical generalizations and particular facts of evolution." (161) Beckner acknowledges that selection theory is not predictive or causal in the logical sense, but he maintains that "one might wish to call an explanation predictive, even if constructed after the fact, whenever the *explanans* lay down sufficient conditions for the *explanandum."* (167) Thus, theory, as used by Beckner and by organismic biologists, differs markedly from the use of theory in the physical sciences.

The organismic biologist, in attempting to explain complex living systems, proposes "that we describe the phenomena exhibited by organic parts in explicit relation to the phenomena exhibited by the wholes, or large systems, of which they are parts, i.e., that we apply to parts concepts defined in terms of phenomena that these parts do not exhibit." (187) Beckner suggests that there are alternatives to this position, usually designated as "mechanistic" descriptions. The test among the alternatives is to be measured by the success in yielding generalizations, and Beckner holds that the organismic point of view is successful. Thus, he has given an account of the prevailing practices of organismic biologists, the concepts they use, and the patterns of explanation which they develop. Nevertheless, he denies what many organismic biologists would affirm—"the intrinsic irreducibility of organic to inorganic phenomena." (190)

10

A SYMPOSIUM
ON THE CONCEPTS
OF BIOLOGY

The report of the conference[1] held at Lee, Massachusetts, in October 1955 was organized and conducted by R. W. Gerard, who contributed two papers to the issue of *Behavioral Science,* which published these articles with an edited transcript of the conference and a selected bibliography as its issue of April 1958.

There were thirteen participants in the conference from the various disciplines of biology. The backgrounds of the participants are reviewed as a part of the conference report. Those taking part were: Frank Brink, Jr., professor of biophysics and dean of graduate studies at the Rockefeller Institute for Medical Research; Ernest W. Caspari, professor of biology at Wesleyan University; R. W. Gerard, professor of neurophysiology at the Mental Health Research Institute, University of Michigan; David R. Goddard, professor of botany and director of the division of botany at the University of Pennsylvania; Rollin D. Hotchkiss, member and professor at the Rockefeller Institute for Medical Research; Ernst Mayr, Alexander Agassiz Professor of Zoology at Harvard University; James G. Miller, professor of psychiatry and director of the Mental Health Research Institute, University of Michigan; Orr E. Reynolds, Director, Office of Science, Office of the

[1] "Concepts of Biology: A Symposium" edited by R. W. Gerard with the assistance of Russell B. Stevens. Based on a conference sponsored by the Biology Council, Division of Biology and Agriculture of the National Academy of Sciences—National Research Council, October 12–14, 1955, and published in *Behavioral Science,* Volume 3, Number 2 (April 1958), pp. 92–215.

Assistant Secretary of Defense (Research and Engineering); Francis
O. Schmitt, Institute Professor of Biology, Massachusetts Institute of
Technology; G. G. Simpson, professor of vertebrate paleontology,
Columbia University; J. N. Spuhler, associate professor of anthropol-
ogy and human genetics, University of Michigan; Paul A. Weiss,
member and professor at the Rockefeller Institute for Medical Re-
search and head of the Laboratory of Developmental Biology; and
Seawell Wright, Leon J. Cole Professor of Genetics, University of
Wisconsin.

Problems Placed before the Conference

In the Foreword to the April 1958 issue of *Behavioral Science,*
Paul A. Weiss, as Chairman of the Biology Council, stated the purposes of the Lee Conference.

The following conference report centers on the question of whether
present-day biology is paying too little attention to its conceptual matura-
tion and, if so, why. . . . Why does contemporary biology show—or, at
least, appear to show—a marked disproportion between sheer empiricism
and conceptual development in disfavor of the latter? Is this a fact or an
illusion? And, if true, is this simply an expression of the relatively
immature state of biology as an objective science; or is it perhaps,
conversely, co-responsible for the prolongation of this state of immatu-
rity? Has the momentum of scientific routine in teaching and research
swept us so far away from the mainsprings of our science that we have
lost sight of the essentially intellectual nature of the scientific process?
And consequently, are we drifting into a habit not only of dispensing with
conceptual ordering, but almost of questioning the respectability of conceptual effort? (93)

In this Foreword, Paul Weiss described concepts as "the structural
elements of . . . [a] growing body of knowledge." One of the tasks
which the Biology Council undertook under his chairmanship was to
exhibit "the organic structure of the body of biological knowledge."
In pursuance of this aim, a committee of the Council put together a
working paper entitled "Concepts and Principles of Biology" for
review by the Council, which determined that it should be sent to all
conference participants. Ralph Gerard, as the writer of this paper,
expressed the hopes and purposes of the Council for the conference:

An examination of the discipline, biology, in terms of its organization,
methods, relations, and particularly its conceptualizations, could serve
many useful ends. Any success in improving the intellectual ordering of

our subject would contribute to improved public relations, to the recruitment of more superior students, and to a better internal structure which would favor better teaching and research and in turn attract more students and support. (95)

His intent in this paper was to present in the form of a dimensional analysis—the methods, disciplines, and concepts of biology which would serve as a starting point for discussion by the conferees. The correctness of terminology used in expressing the intent was later questioned, but the council could not reach a consensus on the issue. In the text of this initial working paper, Gerard's view of dimensional analysis and its values were stated as follows:

Dimensional analysis strongly favors the assigning of precise meanings to terms, encourages comparison of terms of like dimensions and enables one to come at the dimensionless core of concepts, and should encourage a type of scaling that reveals true relationships. . . . Perhaps appropriate scaling of biological times in terms of life spans, expression of variation in terms of standard variance units, an emphasis on topological rather than geometric relationships, and the like would pay great dividends in general biological thinking. (95)

In a sense, Gerard's initial working paper presented a new systematics.

The new systematics may well supply the kind of intellectual skeleton on which to order the previously overwhelming descriptive facts of the old systematics. . . . It may even infuse new meaning, and therefore life and support, into the presently moribund museums—relics of the 19th century interest in collecting and classifying organisms. (97–98)

The Preliminary Outline of Concepts of Biology

Three schemata of biology—methods, disciplines, and concepts —were prepared by Gerard and reviewed by participants prior to their arrival. That the first two of these were given little attention is reflected in the transcript of the conference. The conference turned its full attention to the analysis of concepts. The table which Gerard used to organize his presentation of the concepts of biology had as its y axis the levels of organization. These levels were designated by roman numerals, as follows: "I molecule, II organelle, III cell, IV organ, V individual, VI small group (band), VII species (potentially interbreeding population), VIII community, ecological area, IX total biota." On the x axes of the schemata of concepts were the three categories which follow:

(A) deals with structure or architecture, is concerned with spatial relations, with processes that have become fixed in material forms, and should ultimately cover structure as a type of information or negative entropy, and relate to the degree of determination or stochastic freedom exhibited by the processes which produced it, and also the variance in its relationships. (B) is equilibrium, and is concerned with dynamic equilibrium or flux, and with organisms or orgs as dynamic entities. This also includes the notion of function, of interaction of entities and of responses to stimulation. The last rubric, (C) is concerned with history or origin, the problem of specific synthesis and of local entropy decrease. (98–99)

The following excerpt from his table at the level of organization of the "individual" illustrates the specification introduced in each of the rubrics: (102)

A.	B.	C.
V. Organism (org concept, individual)	V. Open system Homeostasis (physiologic constant)	V. Biogenetic law Learning Remembering
Environment	Stress (limit of	Creative behavior
Specificity	homeostatic	Ideation—new idea
The unconscious	tolerance, factor of safety)	Goals
Consciousness, feeling	Integration	Purpose
Mind	Gradient	
	Adaptive behavior, sensation, gestalts	
	The ego function	
	Volition, freedom	
	Wake—sleep	
	Active—rest	
	Well—sick	

THE NATURE OF BIOLOGY AS REFLECTED IN DISCUSSIONS

Response to the Preliminary Outline

Although all participants in the conference read the initial working paper, there was little focus on it at the conference. During the opening discussion, the participants ranged across their areas of interest and concern in biology, with little consideration to the prepared outline of concepts. In the afternoon of the first day, there was some concentration on selected topics, some congealing of interests in discussions of "order," "organization," "the unique nature of biology," and "concepts." That evening each participant retired to prepare a personal statement on "five principles, concepts, properties, concerning living systems which you feel are relatively major in biology." (136)

The next morning each presented his statement; with the exception of J. N. Spuhler, all participants seemed constrained to make statements rather than present labels. The ensuing discussion brought out one of the essential problems of the conference—that the same label does not elicit the same informational content, even among a group of highly selected individuals whose life work is in the area of biology. An aspect of this problem is most clearly indicated in a statement of Mayr, who said:

We come right here to one of the cruxes of the whole thing. . . . Just how are we going to decide which are the theorems and which are the subtheorems? We will probably have to let time decide that. In other words let us accept Schmitt's word that these are the theorems on the molecular level and the word of Simpson and myself that these are the theorems on the upper level, and thus get something which is properly balanced, because it is a combination of the two extreme viewpoints. (145)

The problem of telescoping ideas, which is an essential part of any scheme of classification, had some of its difficulties elucidated by Hotchkiss as he stated:

It seems to me the only mistake is in telescoping them all. For my taste, ordered heterogeneity is already two thoughts, and ordered coupling of heterogeneity is three. The statement, repetitive production of ordered heterogeneity, that's four. It is comprehensive, but not clarifying, to try to get all four into one sentence—we want to separate them, do we not? (145)

The mutuality needed when specialists working with particular areas try to synthesize the sweep of a discipline was illustrated when Mayr indicated the necessary reciprocity of such an undertaking. As the discussion of principles continued, the differences in meanings began to be apparent, and Gerard was led to remark:

The talk at the end was about communication and information, and I confess to a certain sense of frustration. Over and over again, something was said, quite explicitly by one—and later was repeated by someone else, in slightly different words, as if it were a brand new thought. Why are we failing to communicate with each other to that extent? After we made our separate statements of principles I said we were all stating pretty much the same thing, but each was expanding his own areas. An hour later this statement was made again as if entirely new. There should not have been any great communication problem here. (147)

But such problems of communication did continue throughout the conference; for the most pervasive problem of the conference was the differing meanings and emphases brought to bear by participants with regard to terms such as "order," "organization," "adaptation," "individual," "structure," and "function." The disparities in these points of view have been reviewed elsewhere.[2]

On the final day of the conference, three working groups reported. Their topics of concern were history, function, and structure. Each group attempted to synthesize the thoughts of the conference, or the committee, with regard to the given topic. No general consensus seemed to emerge, but Paul Weiss, in reporting for the Structure committee, concluded his report with the following observations with regard to the committee's work: the committee was ". . . conscious of the fact that there is no sense to the question what comes first— function or structure." In commenting on the schema of Gerard, he concluded for the committee, "Essentially our evaluation has been that, by and large, it's a very workable scheme." (184–185)

While additional comments were to be made during the conference, this seemed to be the essential closing evaluation of the conference. With many ideas left undeveloped and many differences in points of view unresolved, the conference ended with a general agreement as to both the conference's usefulness and the usefulness of Gerard's schema of concepts.

THE NATURE OF BIOLOGY AS INTEGRATED BY GERARD

In Appendix II to the issue of *Behavioral Science* in which the initial working paper and the condensed transcript of the Lee Confer-

[2] James T. Robinson, *An Investigation of Selected Frameworks of Science,* unpublished doctoral dissertation, Stanford University, Stanford, California, 1964.

ence are presented, Ralph W. Gerard's paper on "Units and Concepts of Biology" is reproduced. In a footnote Gerard notes that his paper "rests heavily on the conference on Concepts of Biology (and on working with colleagues at the Mental Health Research Institute) and can serve to help integrate the rich discussion of the conference." (197)

In the scope of this brief article, Gerard summarizes the developmental stages in inquiry, briefly notes the entities of biological inquiry, the levels of organization, and the dimensions of the continuum of the process of change: becoming, being, and behaving.

Developmental Stages of Inquiry

In the first phases of inquiry, man's role is an integral aspect of the known. This first stage of development in inquiry is simple observation and description. It is followed by the taxonomic stage, during which different individuals are seen as possessing certain attributes which provide means for their classification. As attention is directed to the ordered differences within the classes of the taxonomy, finer distinctions and new attributes are seen and the next stage of development is reached, that of morphology. As investigation moves on, special attributes of the object are selected for attention and measurement; manipulation and experiment begin to dominate. As interest increases in the changes of an observable in time, the movement from the morphological to the physiological phase of inquiry is made. Later in the process of inquiry the class of objects may become of greater interest and descriptive morphology is replaced by "comparative morphology or systematics or physiology or genetics or some other discipline concerned with relation or function or development." As attention is thus focused on the class or property, rather than the individual, the "actuarial approach replaces the clinical approach . . . and analysis is added to description." (198–199)

Entities

The entities or units of concern to biologists can be grouped into those "which are invariable (organization) or repetitive (function) or progressive (development) in time." (199)

Levels of Organization

Gerard's discussion of levels in this paper seems essentially to include the material presented in his initial working paper, but a new emphasis is given to the term "org," which he finds useful.

I have found the word *org* convenient for those material systems or entities which are individuals at a given level but are composed of subordinate units, lower level orgs, and which serve as units in superordinate individuals, higher level orgs. The important levels are those whose orgs (entities) are relatively enduring and self-contained. . . . Higher level orgs are likely to have a greater variety than lower order ones, and they are likely to depend more on their particular past; they are more individual. (200)

The Continuum of Change

Gerard discusses the processes of change under the three headings of becoming, being, and behaving.

History, or becoming, . . . is a regular change, normally progressive, in a system along the time axis; function, or behaving, is a repetitive perturbation along this secular trend; and structure, or being, is the instantaneous status. (201)

In order to see the way in which development, as reflected in history, can be related to both the molecular and societal levels of organization, the following quotation is of interest:

A society becomes what it is through learning by its individuals, morphogenetic development by their cells, reduplication with mutation by their genes, and so, by regress, into the domain of chemistry. (202)

The word behaving in this paper is used in parallel to "regulation." Gerard sees "the vast bulk of the functioning of any enduring system is as displacement-correcting responses." Since there is a limit to the amount of displacement a system can assume, some processes become irreversible and structure results—sometimes the structures of pathology and dissolution. (202–203)

Being, or "organization," is discussed as the "ordering of material in space and of events in time" at a particular point in time.

Toward the conclusion of his article, Gerard points out the essential interrelatedness of the processes which have been discussed:

History produces structure, and structure determines function—becoming gives being, and this is capable of behaving; order is produced and maintained—but the relations are so intimate and seemingly reciprocal that the distinctions sometimes seem artificial. (204)

PART 4
FUNDAMENTALS
OF A FRAMEWORK
FOR THE SCIENCE
CURRICULUM

An understanding of science is considered to be an essential outcome of general education in contemporary society. Achieving this educational goal requires comprehension of a useful structure of scientific knowledge. Such a structure may be clarified by making explicit the understandings that characterize scientifically literate individuals.

An artificial dichotomy of products and processes of science reflects the spectator-spectacle doctrine of classical physics but is incompatible with twentieth century science. A shift in perspective, especially a shift in the philosophical perspective with which a teacher interprets natural phenomena to students, requires significant shifts in the patterns of science education.

11

REFLECTIONS ON
THE NATURE
OF SCIENCE

The ideational frameworks developed in six selected writings are synthesized in this chapter into a statement of the nature of scientific knowledge, which may, in turn, serve as a source document for considerations for education in the sciences. This synthesis will not, however, stand alone; the full meaning of its terms and the details of its form are to be sought from the body of this work and from the writings upon which it is based. The formulations presented are limited in two aspects: (1) the small number of writings upon which they are based, and (2) the judgment of the writer in selecting from the totality of the source documents those aspects perceived as being central to the formulation of a statement on the nature of science which is relevant to general education in the sciences.

In his concluding essay in "Concepts of Biology," Ralph Gerard writes of the three enduring aspects around which biology might be organized. He speaks of Becoming, Being, and Behaving. His concern in this essay is with the nature of life, but, by analogy, it seems appropriate to apply this continuum of development to the nature of science—whether physical or biological—presented by each of the writers. Being is seen as the state of the systems of knowledge at a particular moment in time—it is cross-sectional, rather than longitudinal. The process of becoming is seen as the history of knowledge, and the process of behaving consists of the new discoveries and reinterpretations which will themselves in time become a part of the history of knowledge. Gerard's view of the continuity of development, with structure, or *being,* as a slice through processes at a given point in time seems to have application to each of the writings studied. Each writer is concerned not only with the structure of his discipline as seen at the point of his writing; he is also concerned with the changing nature of man's view of the world and the scientist's view of his discipline through time. Each, but perhaps most clearly Margenau, Frank, Bridgman, and Woodger, has sought to clarify both the status of his discipline and the processes by which the current view which he depicts has come about. Thus, in each writing, a structure of the discipline and the processes of inquiry are integrally interwoven. In each, one sees that the assumptions which have been brought together to direct the emerging structure remain to guide inquiry as new problems are faced and new solutions sought; but not only do these assumptions—these metaphysical principles of Margenau; these pragmatic, semantic, and logical properties of Frank—guide; they become embedded in a structural edifice which, at a given point of time, can be termed a structure of a discipline. To read either Gerard or Margenau is to be struck by the power of the idea of "order." Thus, while in the summaries of each writer structure and process have been separated for purposes of clarification, in this summary structure and process will be viewed together as integral parts of an area of knowledge.

As may be apparent, the inclusion of the biological and physical sciences within a single structural framework requires discussion at a high level of abstraction. Such a framework may not seem relevant to science education. On the other hand, acknowledgement of the necessity for such abstraction may assist science educators in examining what they mean by a "science" curriculum.

A VIEW OF THE NATURE OF SCIENCE

Certain commonalities of thought emerge from the writings investigated. The discourse of scientific thought is seen to be carried forth on two distinguishable levels—the empirical and the rational. That the bulk of scientific thought deals with the rational, or constructional, realm is well documented. In both the biological and physical sciences, the "haziness of the immediately given" (to use Margenau's phrase) has been brought under control by methodological procedures—the establishment of operation definitions, rules of correspondence. This methodology provides for the development of a system of constructs with multiple connections (definitions) linking construct to construct and construct to observables. A system of verified constructs and connecting definitions forms a theory which may be axiomatized to form a hierarchical system, with more extensible constructs which are farther from the plane of perception. The logico-mathematical system thus developed—a deductive system—is constantly tested by verification of the consequences of derived hypotheses. Such a system may be falsified; it cannot be proved absolutely true.

Though a fully axiomatized system of theories may be the goal of the various sciences, none of the sciences has fully achieved this level of explanation. In fact, the very methodology which provides for such deductive systems precludes a final explanation, in that those explanatory schemes go beyond the phenomena from which they were constructed. New and more extensible theories are further removed from the plane of perception—indeed, this appears to be the general movement of explanation throughout the sciences, and this movement does not seem to have limits.

Deductive theories characterize the physical sciences, although not all phenomena are explained in their systems of theories. On the other hand, the biological sciences have developed few, if any, axiomatic systems. Woodger was able to axiomatize Mendelian genetics, but most of biology remains correlational. The correlational aspects of scientific explanation are here viewed as including inductive generalizations that are not included in a deductive theory. Such generalizations lie close to the plane of perception, and, in many instances, operational definitions linking constructions with observables have not been developed. In many cases, one suspects that the observables which may be formulated into constructions to build a fully deductive theory remain undiscovered.

If correlational methods were placed at one end of a continuum and the methods of the exact sciences at the other, physics would lie toward the exact science end and the biological sciences toward the correlational end. Neither has patterns belonging exclusively to one or the other. That the movement of both the biological and physical sciences is toward exact, or deductive, explanations is confirmed by all of the writers. Only Beckner states that perhaps the nature of phenomena of interest to organismic biologists precludes deductive systems of explanation at the higher levels of organization in biology. The discussions of both Woodger and Gerard raise serious questions that lead one to question Beckner's view.

If a structure of science selected for developing science curricula is to include the full continuum of correlational and exact procedures, then an extended discussion of the processes of scientific thought and the constraints on reasoning must be added to the brief discussion above. That such a structure should be selected is proposed in the next chapter, which includes the related discussion of the meanings of such a structure for developing scientific literacy.

A VIEW OF THE EXACT SCIENCES

The Organization of Thought

One way of illustrating the organization of thought in the exact sciences is shown in Figure 7.[1] This schema is taken primarily from the study of Frank's work, but it incorporates some aspects of the writings by other physical scientists.

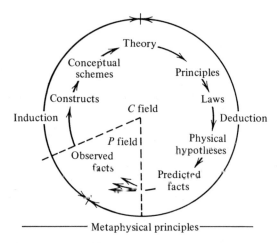

Figure 7. *A schema of the organization of thought in the physical sciences.*

This circle of thought "begins," "ends," and "continues" in the area of observation as a way of emphasizing the empirical nature of the exact sciences. But observed facts are not given; they are selected

[1] The reader is reminded that diagrams "are not universal statements and cannot completely take the place of such statements. . . . A diagram is a particular object and cannot possibly represent all that a universal general statement asserts." Woodger, *op. cit.,* pp. 179–180.

by the scientist from a background of contemporary theory, general principles, and metaphysical or pragmatic components. Through inductive processes, generalizations of various kinds are developed. Two seemingly distinct groups of such generalizations may be distinguished here and will be developed somewhat more fully in the conclusion to this chapter. Some inductions yield general statements which, in the main, result from abstracting or correlating selected observations into groupings or classes. The physical, or exact, sciences are characterized by inductions which include inventive, imaginative qualities going beyond the observations which generated their development. Such statements were variously referred to as "hypotheses," "concepts," or "constructs." This kind of statement (the term "construct" is adopted for such statements) is not produced at random but emerges under the constraints of the theory within which it is formed. Logical, mathematical, and metaphysical constraints function throughout the invention and early development of the construct and in the processes of verification to which it is subjected. These constraints continue to function as the construct is fitted into the total area of discourse in which it is relevant. Metaphor and analogy are often used in the early phases of construction; but as the testing proceeds, the precision of terminology is increased as ambiguity is reduced and metaphor and analogy are removed.

Verification proceeds from the P field, with the aid of correlations, to the C field with its network of acceptable constructs, where it moves into what are generally referred to as deductive processes—the prediction of new observations in the P field. It is here that prediction fails or succeeds. The predicted observations must fall within the probability prescribed by the theory of which they are a part. When this circuit is successfully completed, the entire set of constructs involved is said to be verified. But the scientist seeks to predict more data than those which formed the original observation; he seeks deductive fertility and a nontrivial return to the P field.

The establishment of correspondences between constructs and observations provides epistemic connections between the logical, rational areas of thought and the empirical, observational areas which give substance to constructs. As verification proceeds, correlations between constructs may result in relations expressible in the form of differential equations, the criteria for a law of nature as it is used in its most precise formulation.

Thus the goal of exact scientific explanation is seen to be the development of a coherent logico-mathematical system of relations between symbols, that is, epistemic and constitutive definitions between symbols, such that the logical conclusions drawn from these statements of relations become statements about observable facts that are confirmed by actual sense observations. The development of such a deductive system serves not only to predict new facts, but it also serves to guide the knower in carrying out observations.

The acceptance of deductive theories which lie close to the plane of perception (P plane in Figure 8) is based primarily upon the logical, semantical, and empirical relations of the theory. As theories are formulated which lie further from the P plane and which are more extensible—theories of higher generality, in Frank's terms—acceptance is based upon more than these scientific criteria; the psychological and sociological climates in which they are formulated become a part of the criteria for acceptance.

The Constructed Nature of Reality

The preceding discussion has developed a physical reality which is viewed as constructed. Further development of support for this position will be discussed with the aid of the schema in Figure 8.

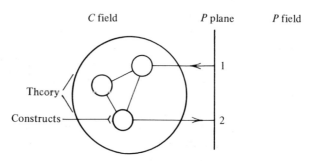

Figure 8. *The circuit of verification.*

Source: Adapted from Margenau, *op. cit.*, Fig. 6.1, p. 106.

Sense data at "1" are selected from all the possible observables to define a construct. The selection of observables requires special attention. Throughout this presentation, the constraints of logic, mathematics, and metaphysical principles have been shown to affect the choice of those observables regarded as significant. The level of sophistication of instruments available and those deemed by scientists as appropriate for use with the phenomena under investigation provide further constraints upon the selection of those observables used to define the construct. The selected observables of the P field stand in adjectival relation to the constructs they define. They, unlike the constructs which give them meaning, are measurable. They are tied to constructs by rules of correspondence. In the C field, the construct must fit into the logical relations of existing theory. Prediction back to the P plane at "2" must be through new pathways to new observations—it must be nontrivial in Margenau's sense. Thus, prediction involves both empirical and rational knowledge; neither is sufficient alone. It is this deductive fertility which characterizes the organization of thought in the exact sciences—an organization which finds structure and process so inextricably entwined. Through the development of operational definitions, correspondence of the rational and the empirical is attained. Throughout this circuit, the observer is an integral part of both what is observed and what is constructed. One has only to recall the changes in man's conception of motion to be reminded of this essential relationship.

Even though the discussion above considered the processes of verification within accepted theory, these same processes are found in the development of new theories. It is hoped that the difficulties accompanying the development of new theoretical structures become apparent upon reflection. Discovery in science is thus seen as a dual event involving the selection of the crucial observables and the establishment of relations among them.

A VIEW OF THE CORRELATIONAL SCIENCES

The Organization of Thought

The selected writings by biological scientists present a greater divergence in terminology and a wider range in points of view than do the writings by the physical scientists. Thus, the discussion which follows does not present the unified and cohesive pattern of thought which characterized the writings in the physical sciences.

In attempting to understand the nature of organisms, the biological sciences begin with a descriptive stage, in which organisms are described and grouped. This taxonomic stage is supplemented by a structural or morphological stage during which relations are sought.

Further investigations proceed to a stage of inquiry into the dynamics of living systems and then finally to the holistic stage. Each of these stages of inquiry may proceed simultaneously in a particular branch of the biological sciences, but as descriptive knowledge has grown, the movement of inquiry has been to the morphological, physiological, and finally the holistic stage. This concern with the whole organism has led biologists to analyze the living state through specification of levels of organization—molecular, organelle, cell, organ, individual, small group, population, and community—and through the relationships which link these levels. Investigation at each level has produced large bodies of discrete facts and concepts, but the ordering of these facts and concepts into theoretical frameworks has lagged. A major thrust in the works by biologists is toward the logico-mathematical theory of the model of the exact sciences as the desirable form of theoretical framework for explaining living systems. At the same time, some biologists hold to the uniqueness of life and continue to question the applicability of the techniques of the exact sciences at all levels of biological organization, especially at the higher levels.

In Beckner's work, the position of the organismic biologists is presented. The significant problems for ordering thought about phenomena at the higher levels of organization are seen to be organization, history, and purpose. Beckner presents a status study of the "way of thought" by which organismic biologists "explain" organization, history, and purpose in living systems; but, as is pointed out, such explanations do not include concepts which may become part of deductive theory. In the writer's view, the works by Woodger and Gerard illustrate the thrust within biological thought which is characterized by the search for new ways of considering the living state so that fully axiomatized theories may eventually be developed.

Woodger was able to axiomatize Mendelian genetics by developing a symbolic system and applying the laws of thought developed by Boole and Frege. He presents a process of theory building in which levels of hypotheses are ordered by the consequence relation into a hierarchical system. He proposes that such methodological approaches could produce deductive theories which would embrace more of the subject matter of the biological sciences. This attempt illustrates a second major thrust in biological thought common to the works used in this study. This thrust is the search for ways in which the levels of organization may be linked. The Lee Conference discussion of "adaptation" eloquently points up the problems of investigations which proceed at a single level but use the language developed at another level for seemingly similar phenomena without taking a next step and specifying the operational, rather than the analogical, meanings of the language used.

Gerard presents a pattern of thinking about the living state as a function of time which is represented by the writer in Figure 9 below.

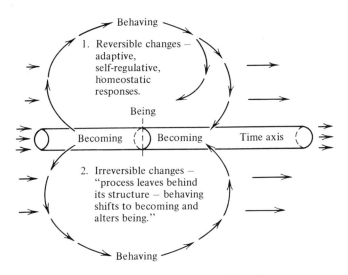

Figure 9. *A schema representing Gerard's conception of the organism.*

The history, or becoming, of the system is the regular change of the system with time. Becoming, thus, incorporates those processes of behaving which become irreversible and result in structure. The organization, or being, of the system may be thought of as an instantaneous cross section through the time axis. The behavior of the system includes both reversible and irreversible changes. The schema represents the whole organism and each of the levels of organization.

The Patterns of Explanation

The flow of discussion presented in the transcript of the Lee Conference dramatically illustrates the problems Woodger sought to solve through his analyses of the activities of biologists. By distinguishing observation records from hypotheses and by giving attention to the function of language in biological explanation, Woodger provides a methodological approach for producing a brief and fully generalizable scientific language to be used in dealing with the living state. By using a combination of algebra and the system of shared and unshared names, Woodger demonstrates the feasibility of freeing biological statements from dependence upon the physical language without abandoning explanatory schemes fashioned on the pattern of the exact sciences.

Beckner shows that historical and teleological explanations are characteristic of biological explanations for systems at the higher levels of organization. He finds teleological explanation useful and perhaps necessary at those levels, but the discussion of the Lee Conference points up both the desire of biologists to eliminate teleological language from their explanatory schemes and the possibility of doing so. This thought was most concisely stated by Gerard, who sees purpose entering biological statements "not in the sense of a purposer, but in the sense that the significance of events is understood in terms of the future more easily than in terms of the past."[2]

The concern of biologists with the fragmentation of their discipline into many noncommunicating subdisciplines, with special concepts and special language, has brought about a search for concepts which can be operationally defined and ordered into deductive systems. Information theory, systems analysis, symbolic logic, and the laws of thought developed by Boole and Frege, along with the methodology of the exact sciences, are the areas of interest to biologists seeking to explain the living state. It is of interest here to quote from Margenau who, in discussing "causation in biology," states:

In biology, multiplicity of causal schemes is probably important enough to be studied in its own right. It may give rise to levels of explanation, perhaps an entire hierarchy of explanations, each a causal one, and each at a different stage of organizational integration. Thus, there may be encountered a thing framable in terms of molecules and molecular forces, another in terms of thermodynamic systems, another in which cells and cytological interaction are basic concepts, and perhaps one that speaks of stimuli and responses. If a prognosis can be based upon physics, one may judge it to be a very long time before the vertical connections between these schemes are completely understood.[3]

[2] Gerard, *op. cit.*, p. 141.
[3] Margenau, *op. cit.*, p. 417.

12

CONSIDERATIONS

FOR EDUCATION

IN THE SCIENCES

The broad framework of a structure of science, with the continuum of correlational and exact procedures, must now be further clarified and extended. In order to relate educational implications with the proposed structure of science, this extension will include the related educational considerations. An assumption guiding the selection of material to be presented in this discussion is that the development of an "understanding" of science is an important goal of education. If our society requires "scientific literacy,"[1] then the writer proposes that some of the central elements of "understanding" and "scientific literacy" consistent with the nature and organization of scientific knowledge as formulated through this investigation would include those discussed below.

Scientists, science educators, and science teachers have recognized the complex problems of revising science curricula so that they may be more in keeping with the nature of scientific knowledge. The work of James B. Conant at Harvard as developed at the college level in *On Understanding Science: An Historical Approach*[2] and, more recently,

---

[1] The voluminous literature on this subject will not be reviewed here, but readers are referred to such writings as *Education in the Age of Science,* Brand Blanshard (ed.) (New York: Basic Books, Inc., 1959); *The Challenge of Science Education,* Joseph S. Roucek (ed.) (New York: Philosophical Library, 1959); and the writings of Bentley Glass, Joseph Schwab, J. Robert Oppenheimer, Jacob Bronowski, and many others.

[2] (New York: The New American Library, A Mentor Book, 1951).

the work of the Physical Science Study Committee,[3] the Chemical Bond Approach,[4] the Chemical Education Materials Study,[5] and the Biological Sciences Curriculum Study[6] at the secondary school level have each proposed new curricula for education in the sciences. Other studies are being developed for the elementary grades; for example, the Commission on Science Instruction of the American Association for the Advancement of Science has developed and is sponsoring the testing of materials for a K-6 program entitled *Science—A Process Approach.*[7] These studies and others have emphasized the conceptual nature of science and have given special emphasis to the processes of inquiry which characterize the scientific enterprise. The works of these groups, with the exception of Conant's material, have become available since the inception of this investigation. In the writer's view, the findings of this study go beyond the published statements of these groups by providing a more comprehensive treatment of the nature and organization of scientific knowledge.

THE CONSTRUCTIONIST NATURE OF SCIENTIFIC THOUGHT

Although the sciences may be seen to consist of observation, experiment, and hypotheses, the findings of this investigation support a necessity to go beyond this simple formulation in developing an understanding of the nature of science; for such an understanding must go far beyond the common-sense meanings of these terms.

Man himself, as he conducts his observations, is an organized observer and a searcher for order. Thus, the observer enters into the construction of scientific knowledge as he observes phenomena and selects those elements of experience which may be constructed into ordered systems of explanation. A theory guides observation, al-

[3] Stephen White, "The Physical Science Study Committee, (3) The Planning and Structure of the Course," *Contemporary Physics,* II (October 1960), 39–54.

[4] Laurence E. Strong, "Facts, Students, Ideas," *Journal of Chemical Education,* XXXIX (March 1962), 126–129.

[5] Glenn T. Seaborg, "The Chemical Education Materials Study," *Chemical Education Materials Study Newsletter,* I (November 1960), 1.

[6] *Biology Teachers' Handbook,* Joseph J. Schwab (Supervisor of Writing Team) (New York: John Wiley & Sons, Inc., 1963).

[7] "Science in the Kindergarten and Early Grades," *Science Education News,* American Association for the Advancement of Science, Miscellaneous Publication No. 63–20, November 1963.

though the investigators may be unaware of both the theory within which he investigates and the metaphysical principles permeating the theory. Observations may generate hypotheses which may be extensions of existing theory, or they may become generative of new experiments and hypotheses which may eventuate in the modification or replacement of the theory within which they had their origins.

The theories of science have been shown to be constructed, and their validity may be considered adequate so long as their predictions are confirmed in experiment—in this sense they may be considered as hypotheses. Theories are not as long lived as the metaphysical principles which contributed to their formulation. Theories have been shown to have logical coherence; to consist of an interlocking web of constructs and laws; to be related to each other by definitions, or, in the case of laws, by differential equations; and to relate to experience through rules of correspondence—operational definitions.

Accordingly, an individual who is developing scientific literacy will increasingly

1. *understand* that the thrust in all science is for them to become increasingly theoretical and exact, the biological sciences being currently more correlational and the physical sciences more exact, and

    understand the current theoretical framework of the exact sciences, and where such frameworks are developed in the largely correlational sciences;

    understand that the relevance and validity of the constructs of a science are determined by the theoretical structure of science;

    understand that no construct is considered valid until it can be fitted into an existing theory and function successfully in facilitating scientific prediction;

    understand the movement of scientific theories considered to explain "why" to become in the course of time to be considered as descriptions of "how";

    understand the limitations of current patterns of explanation in the biological sciences and understand the attempts to devise explanatory systems which will be predictive.

2. *understand* the inextricable relationship of the knower and the known, and

understand the relative longevity of metaphysical principles, theories, laws of nature, and constructs within the evolution of scientific knowledge, and

understand how changes in metaphysical principles can bring about profound changes in the structure of scientific knowledge;

understand that scientific knowledge has developed as a result of semantical, logical, and pragmatic components, and

understand that those aspects of experience of interest to science are those which satisfy the available procedures for rationalizing data.

3. *understand* the contemporary status of constructs, that is, what operations define the constructs, what constructs are equally supported by these operations, and what other factors give preference to the preferred constructs.

More generally, the individual who understands science will increasingly understand that the processes of setting up theories from which facts and applications of facts can be derived is what is meant by science today.[8]

MAN'S VIEW OF THE UNIVERSE
AND THE NATURE OF SCIENCE

The rejection of the spectator-spectacle doctrine and its replacement in modern science by man as the interpreter of nature requires special attention to the relations between phenomena, signs, and symbols. But these relations have not been static; rather they have slowly shifted, and at certain points in the history of mankind, the changes have come with dramatic swiftness. The currents of scientific thought which questioned the organismic universe of the Greeks and resulted in the Copernican Revolution and the world machine of Newton took place over centuries within the fabric of the evolving society of Western Civilization but not without times of social turmoil and philosophic controversy. An understanding of the interrelations of

---

[8] It has not been possible to provide in this work complete substantiation for all of the understandings which will be presented in this chapter. Interested readers are referred to the writer's dissertation or to the original works for this substantiation.

scientific thought with the social milieu in which it is embedded is a necessary part of education in the sciences. Though scientists in the past three centuries have been more concerned with the semantic and logical components of scientific theories, the social and psychological (pragmatic) components have been a continuing part of the growth and development of scientific knowledge.

Philipp Frank stressed that it is the work of the philosophy of science to find out how we get from our common-sense view of the world to the principles of science. Until such understanding is accomplished, we have specialists who cannot speak to one another and ignorant but learned people who can deal in compartmentalizations of knowledge without feeling any necessity to assist mankind toward the development of a world view consistent with knowledge in science.

It thus becomes essential that education in the sciences provide ways for individuals to learn that the very "seeing" and "recording" that man does have been influenced by his past. The signs which denote phenomena are themselves inventions and are not the phenomena.

Accordingly, an individual who is developing scientific literacy will increasingly

1. *understand* the way in which other areas of man's thinking or beliefs in religion, logic, mathematics, technology, etc., may influence his views in an area of science, and

   understand that science after 1600 was closely allied with technology and scientists sought to derive the general principles of physics from the laws of nature ("principles of intermediate generality") rather than from "intelligible principles,"

   understand that the work in the philosophy of science, in contrast to the work of science, is devoted to providing a system of concepts and laws within which science, philosophy, and the humanities can fit, and

   understand the distinction and historical derivation of "intelligible principles" as contrasted with "general principles of physical science."[9]

2. *understand* the way in which science makes contributions to man's common-sense view of his world.

[9] See Frank, *op. cit.*, for elaboration of these statements.

3. *understand* the inability of science alone to decide on the validity of theories of very high generality.

4. *understand* that it is the responsibility of the scientist to be able to interpret the consequences of his work for man's common-sense view of the world.

More generally, the individual who understands science will increasingly understand that growth toward wisdom in science leads one to place science within a total framework of human thought.

THE PROCESSES OF SCIENTIFIC REASONING

Selected aspects of the processes of scientific reasoning important to understanding the "constructional nature of scientific thought" are presented here in order to develop and clarify their essential relationships within the structure of science. The reader is referred to Parts 2 and 3 of this investigation and to the original works for a more complete explication of these relationships.

Within the structure of science, the processes of induction and deduction are seen to enter into the form of the structure in a web-like—as contrasted with a linear—order. The scientist collects observations and then proceeds by "induction" to hypotheses. This creation from observational material of a structure of "linguistic material" includes more than the observational material; for theories, ideas, and thoughts play an essential role in induction and furnish raw materials which may be shaped by imagination into new constructs.

Inductions which lead eventually to deductions within established theory are to be distinguished from inductive generalizations which summarize or describe but do not predict. Thus it can be seen why it is said that discoveries come to the well-prepared mind.

Emphasis on validation distinguishes modern from ancient science. The passage from data to constructs to the prediction of new facts within a formal system constitutes the inductive-deductive cycle. However, for the verification of predictions, purely logical deductions are correlated with physical objects by means of operational definitions.

Accordingly, an individual who is developing scientific literacy will increasingly

1. *understand* the distinction in structure and development as between the inductive and deductive aspects of theory and under-

stand that if there were not both of these phases all statements regarding a theory would be analytically equivalent, and

understand that all conceptual schemes are built up from inductions which in turn have been in part achieved through prior deductions from existing theories,

understand that in their inductive organization theories are structured by the consequence relation and in their deductive analysis by the definability relation,[10]

understand that the working scientist invents his signs in order to make presentations of phenomena—the relationships between these signs and symbols and the objects of interest to scientists constitute the semantical component of science,

understand the deductive fertility which emerges from the interplay of two modes of definition, constitutive and epistemic, and

understand the differences in deductive theory and inductive generalizations.

2. *understand* the multidimensional nature of physical concepts, i.e., instrumental, paper-and-pencil, and verbal operations may each contribute to the definition of concepts, and

understand that there is a hiatus between the instrumental and paper-and-pencil operations which cannot be closed,

understand the "haziness" of measurement and the operations used by scientists in the development of concepts,

understand the role of various operations, mathematical convenience, simplicity, and common sense in the acceptance of physical concepts, and

understand that each object is seen as being time extended.

3. *understand* the processes by which physicists verify physical concepts, and

understand that science has selected as its criteria for truth sense data which can be comprehended and checked by everybody with the appropriate training,

understand that principles are confirmed through their consequences (principle + operational definitions of terms = physical hypothesis), and

---

[10] See Woodger, *op. cit.,* for a discussion of these relations.

understand that the principles of physics can only be valid when they refer to a system, or systems, of reference.

More generally, the individual who understands science will increasingly understand the to and fro of induction and deduction and the processes of verification.

The foregoing list of general understandings regarding the processes of scientific reasoning grow out of the analysis of all of the writings considered in this study. The most strongly divergent thinking was reflected in the writing of Morton Beckner, who was concerned with documenting and clarifying the processes for rationalizing data now current in the field of organismic biology. In the symposium included in the issue of *Behavioral Science* in which Gerard's two articles appeared, some of the same strands of thought were in evidence. While the biological sciences are at present more generally correlative or descriptive, the movement toward deductive theories is clearly evident at the lower levels of organization. The applicability of deductive systems at the higher levels of organization is questioned by many biologists. Thus, a thorough understanding of science at this period in history must include understanding of the divergent ways of thought which characterize contemporary biology.

Accordingly, an individual who is developing scientific literacy will increasingly

1. *understand* the development of inquiry in biology with movement from simple observation, to taxonomy, to descriptive morphology, to comparative morphology, and to the addition of analysis to description, and

   understand the diversity of methodological approaches in which practicing biologists are attempting to explain living organisms, and

   understand that some biologists accept noncausal explanations (in the Humean sense) as being currently satisfactory,

   understand that some biologists admit polytypic concepts into law-like statements which may be included in theories which preclude prediction in the sense usually required by theories in the physical sciences,

   understand that some biologists utilize model-explanations and theories made up of families of models and currently see these as the only theories in some areas of biological inquiry;[11] and

understand that functional analyses, so widely used in biology, do not produce explanatory schemes which can become parts of theories in an exact science, and that such a methodology may not be capable of yielding such explanatory schemes.

2. *understand* the logical, mathematical, and syntactical structure of the physical sciences since the physical sciences are being used as a paradigm of the exact, or deductive, sciences, and

understand that some biologists are trying to move toward deductive patterns of thought and to the development of deductive theories;

understand that some areas of biological study are currently more deductively fruitful (genetics, open systems analysis) than are other areas of inquiry; and

understand that a system of classification is not a deductive system although it may provide suggestions as to relevant relationships.

THE CONSTRAINTS WITHIN REASONING

Analysis of the selected writings investigated in this study led the writer to identify and briefly consider certain constraints which over the centuries have become important aspects of the processes of scientific reasoning. These constraints guide and limit the scientist as he observes, experiments, and formulates hypotheses. As guides and constraints they become a part of the structure of science.

Assumptions

The structure of science does not rest exclusively with empirical, logical, and semantical processes. The underlying search for order, the imposition of the metaphysical principles upon constructs, and the influences of the psychological and sociological components on the acceptance of theories of high generality interact with these processes to form the emergent structure of science at a particular point in time.

Accordingly, an individual who is developing scientific literacy will increasingly

---

[11] See Beckner, *op. cit.*, for elaboration of these statements.

understand the continuing role that certain metaphysical principles have had in directing inquiry, and

> understand that the laws of physics deal with incomplete cycles within what may be a totality of no cycles.

Observational, Operational Analysis

Observation plays a key role in science with theory building beginning and ending in observables. The development of new methods of observation—in many instances the development of instruments—extends the range of observations. At the same time, instrumental methods have contributed to the recognition that man, the ordered observer, interprets the "tracings on the paper" and the "spots on the photographic plate." These constraints on observation have resulted in a methodology incorporating operational procedures in which the operations performed in securing the data from which constructs are developed have become recognized as a part of the theoretical structure itself. Thus, as the writers make clear, the eventual emergence of an inductive-deductive scheme with operational procedures which can be checked by anyone with the proper training and equipment is an essential constraint within scientific reasoning.

Accordingly, an individual who is developing scientific literacy will increasingly

1. *understand* the inextricable relationship of the knower and the known, and

    > understand the role of an ordered observer as a constructor of reality.

2. *understand* the relationship of theory to observation—without theory man does not know what to observe.

3. *understand* the significance of state variables, the fields in which the significant variables (the variables of state) have not been discovered and which are, for that reason, complex and intractable.

4. *understand* the role of operational definitions in prediction, for prediction is only possible when the terms within the principles of science have been given their operational definitions.

5. *understand* the ways in which different operations reinforce and supplement each other.

6. *understand* the role of operational analysis as it has come to be a part of the methodology of the physical sciences.

7. *understand* the critical role of instrumental operations in developing physical content in physical concepts.

8. *understand* the nature of operations performed by scientists in developing explanations of natural phenomena.

9. *understand* the impossibility of divorcing physical concepts from the operations by which they are generated and the impossibility of speaking of things existing by themselves in their own rights, and

   understand that no observation record is understandable without knowledge of the theory which underlies the instruments used in observation.

10. *understand* that the available and created instruments are part of the constructional activity through which an observer carries forward experimentation that results in a further definition of reality.

Language

In the recording of observations and in the formulation of constructs, the languages used in the sciences enter the picture. The imprecision of natural languages has become increasingly evident; and as the sciences have become theoretical, more precise languages— including special terms which are operationally defined—have replaced the natural languages. Those sciences which remain primarily correlational, such as biology, retain much of the natural language which uses such terms as "heredity" and "environment" and bring with their use imprecision and ambiguity. The problem of using the physical language with its resulting dualism has been well documented.

As scientific investigation has penetrated into the subatomic area, the value of the extensional, rather than the intensional, point of view has been clearly demonstrated. Although the extensional use of language does not enable the scientist to avoid the use of property words, it does provide for set membership rather than property possession. Empirically specified properties—properties defined by operational definitions—have enabled scientists to avoid the use of abstract entities in clarifying the meaning of constructs. This achievement is not accomplished at the outset of new discoveries but becomes a part of reducing the ambiguities of constructs as they are subjected to the rigors of verification.

In attempting to understand, and indeed to make possible, new discoveries, phenomena are many times related to known experience by analogy. It is here that metaphor and anthropomorphic terms may enter scientific language. Analogies to common-sense language are useful in bringing in certain intuitional elements to provide meaning for new phenomena, but they become harmful if they are regarded as strictly scientific statements rather than as analogies. Like metaphor, they are makeshift, and they substitute for genuine scientific statements. In dealing with organisms, inferring "purpose" and speaking of "function" may be considered similarly as useful devices in making "intelligible" complex phenomena.

Accordingly, an individual who is developing scientific literacy will increasingly

1. *understand* the indispensability of language as well as equipment—that the recording of observations and the creation of hypotheses are impossible without each.

2. *understand* the decreasing utility of the natural language as science develops and the requirements for developing a more precise language; and

   understand the pitfalls into which one may fall in the use of natural language in science—dualistic thinking, unwarranted use of metaphor, elliptical expressions;

   understand that it is only when one utilizes one language that reduction is possible in seeking to compare theories—when languages are mixed, only interpretability is possible in making comparisons;

   understand that, if science wishes to remain within the domain of the physical language, there are many phenomena with which it is impossible to deal—those areas which require the use of the sensible object language, person language, and community language; and

   understand the distinction between shared and unshared names and that a controllable language applicable to the phenomena of interest to biologists can be developed which includes these names, five sentential connectives and the rules for their manipulation, and abbreviators.

3. *understand* the role of man as an interpreter of Nature and that, as a consequence, the study of language is as essential to the scientist as the study of observation, and

> understand the value of a nominalistic position which seeks clarification of relations, utilizes the extensional point of view, and draws upon contributions of Boole and Frege in constructing a more controllable language, and providing a logic of three calculuses; and

> understand the values of asking about any word: What is its extension? What is its degree?[12]

4. *understand* the metaphysical and organismic interpretations which were a part of man's attempt to build explanatory schemes and that modern physical science still exhibits such reasoning, and

> understand that philosophical interpretations of theories grow out of analogies to daily life and are not uniquely determined by the theory.

5. *understand* the use of metaphor and analogy when referring to "directiveness" in organisms as being like "conscious purposing" in man—a yet to be clarified area of methodological concern in biology, and

> understand the use of analogy as a method of discovery, but also understand its lack of complete and unique correspondence.

Logic and Mathematics

All writers have stressed the logical patterns of thought which guide the structuring of the statements produced within inquiry and have stressed the essential logical and mathematical aspects of deductive processes. The development of modern physics has been partly a consequence of the breadth of the mathematics which it has encompassed. Woodger has suggested that the contributions of the Boole-Frege movement might similarly provide the biological sciences with rules of thought for the manipulation of symbols denoting the entities of its complex systems.

[12] See Woodger, *op. cit.*, pp. 255–319, for an explanation of the seven preceding statements.

Accordingly, an individual who is developing scientific literacy will increasingly

1. *understand* that the essential relationships within all exact, or deductive, sciences are logical and mathematical, and

   understand that without the utilization of set theory the biologist is left with properties which he often treats as though they were entities.[13]

2. *understand* the "haziness" of measurement.

3. *understand* the development of a natural law as a statement which has evolved from a definition to a differential equation in which each term has independent instrumental significance.

Prediction, Confirmation, Validity

The search for a science of increasingly precise predictability, rather than a correlational or descriptive science, was evidenced in each of the works studied. That prediction does not seek merely to call forth the original observation but that it must also have the power, or deductive fertility, to be extended to as yet unknown phenomena was stressed by those writers who delved deepest into its meanings. The difficulties of prediction in biology, where the unique event is of interest, brings additional difficulties to this field which are as yet unresolved through available mathematical and logical techniques.

Accordingly, an individual who is developing scientific literacy will increasingly

1. *understand* the differences in criteria used for assessing the validity of a theory and for confirming the theory.

2. *understand* that prediction is only possible when the terms within the principles of science have been given their operational definitions.

3. *understand* that a prediction, to be of value and interest in science, must be able to predict a large number of apparently unrelated observations.

4. *understand* that prediction is made more difficult in biology by the "unique" event and that appropriate logical, mathematical, and

---

[13] See Woodger, *op. cit.*, for illustrations of the use of set theory in biology.

syntactical procedures will be needed to cope with explanatory, or deductive, theories and processes in which such "unique" events may need to be provided for.

Models, Visualizations

The constraints which man's seeming desire to "see" or make "concrete" the phenomena of interest to him result often in his creation of models (dynamic, linguistic, mathematical, mechanical, etc.). In the works studied, the influence of the level of technological development is clearly seen in the mechanical views of Newton or Maxwell, the "enlightened" plumber of Woodger's Harvey, and the computer models of contemporary science. As science has developed, its models have become increasingly theoretical and abstract.

Accordingly, an individual who is developing scientific literacy will increasingly

1. *understand* the use of models and visualizations by the scientist to assist him in organizing his relationships into a unified whole and to assist him in the formulation of hypotheses.

2. *understand* the term "model" as it is used in science to illustrate various sets of relationships that may be linguistic, mathematical, mechanical, etc.

3. *understand* the term "model" as it is used in the biological sciences in the phrase "a family of models" to define a theory that serves to interrelate concepts at different levels of organization.[14]

4. *understand* the organization of biological concepts by means of a two-dimensional grid, with levels of organization on one axis and "being: organization"; "behaving: regulation"; and "becoming: history" on the other axis as a pattern of visualization.

INTUITION AND DISCOVERY

In reviewing these two aspects of scientific thought as expressed in the six writings studied, it is impossible to separate them from the matrix of thought patterns and processes that characterize scientific reasoning; for each works within the total fabric of thought. One becomes convinced from these writings that these processes are the

[14] See Beckner, *op. cit.*, pp. 32–54 for a discussion of "model" as described here.

fruit of imagination developed as a part of a well-prepared mind. Both involve the ability to see relationships previously unseen, but both must work within the semantical, logical, and pragmatic parameters of scientific reasoning. Intuition, particularly, functions in the inductive phase of inquiry when, as Woodger notes, the particularity of the observation record is transcended by the formulation of the zero-level hypothesis which speaks of "all" in reference to a given set of phenomena. Discovery, too, functions within the inductive phase of inquiry and can, also, be an outgrowth of the deductive phase as whole new cosmologies are constructed. Discovery is frequently aided in the inductive phase by analogy and metaphor as the scientist seeks to transcend his observations and achieve a more general statement. Yet, in the last analysis, the insights gained from both of these processes must be integrated and formalized into the accepted patterns of reasoning if they are in time to become a part of the deductive structure of the particular discipline.

Accordingly, an individual who is developing scientific literacy will increasingly

1. *understand* the use of analogy as a method of discovery, but understand its lack of complete and unique correspondence.

2. *understand* the use of imagination and abstraction, which are essential characteristics of the processes of discovery in science.

3. *understand* the value of a language that is deliberately constructed and appropriate for serving as a check on unaided intuition and for extending the scope of intuition.

SUMMARY

The inextricable relationships between structure and process as they emerge from the findings of this study are represented in Figure 10. This schema is an attempt to present the pervasive influences of the metaphysical principles and the circuit of verification as they have been expressed historically and are expressed in contemporary experimental inquiry. It is also an attempt to convey the dynamic and emergent nature of the structure of science developed in this work.

The series of understandings of the structure of science presented in this chapter are proposed as a basis for the development of science curricula which would reflect the structure and organization of scien-

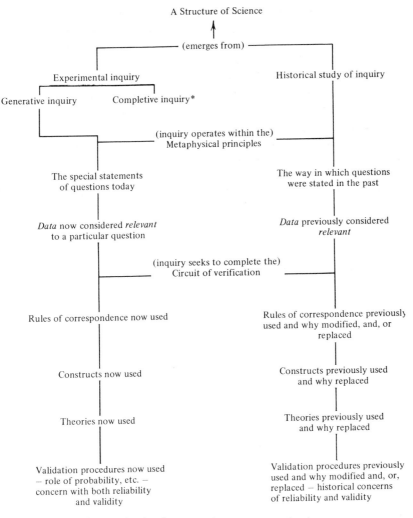

Figure 10. *A schemata of a structure of science.*

* J. J. Schwab made similar distinctions as to type of inquiry in a recent publication, "Education and the Structure of the Disciplines," a paper prepared for the Project on the Instructional Program of the Public Schools, National Education Association, Washington, D.C.

The writer uses the term "generative" in preference to Schwab's "fluid" and "completive" in preference to "stable," in the belief that these terms convey more of the findings of this study than do Schwab's terms. Schwab also uses "Inquiry into inquiries" in a way somewhat parallel to "Historical Study of Inquiry."

tific thought. The structure of science developed from the writings of the scientists provides for a uniting of the methods of inquiry with the knowledge produced. Such a structure, without a process-product dichotomy, would reflect the nature and organization of scientific knowledge as developed through this work.

The convergences in scientific thought that characterize the writings discussed need further investigation to determine whether these apparent convergences can be sustained, enriched, or modified. Claims for the teaching of the structure of science were presented earlier, but, as Bruner indicated, the claims need investigation; for, in order for such claims to be implemented in the educational process, a structure of science must be first elucidated and then translated into educational goals and interpreted in terms of developmental behavioral descriptions for different levels of educational attainment.

BIBLIOGRAPHY

Adrian, E. D. "Science and Human Nature," *Bulletin of the Atomic Scientist,* X (November 1959), 338–341.

Beckner, Morton. *The Biological Way of Thought.* New York: Columbia University Press, 1959.

Biology Teachers' Handbook. Joseph J. Schwab (Supervisor of Writing Team). New York: John Wiley & Sons, Inc., 1963.

Bridgman, Percy W. *The Nature of Some of Our Physical Concepts.* New York: Philosophical Library, 1952.

Bronowski, Jacob. "Knowledge and Education," *Library Journal,* LXXXIII (February 1, 1958), 337–342.

Bruner, Jerome. *The Process of Education.* Cambridge, Mass.: Harvard University Press, 1961.

The Challenge of Science Education. Joseph S. Roucek (ed.). New York: Philosophical Library, 1959.

Conant, James B. *On Understanding Science.* New York: The New American Library, a Mentor Book, 1951.

"Concepts of Biology," a symposium edited by Ralph W. Gerard. *Behavioral Science,* III, No. 2 (1958), 92–215.

Dobzhansky, Theodosius. "Changing Man," *Science,* CLV (January 27, 1967), 409–414.

Education in the Age of Science. Brand Blanshard (ed.). New York: Basic Books, Inc., 1959.

Education and the Structure of Knowledge. Stanley Elam (ed.). Chicago: Rand McNally & Company, 1964.

Form and Strategy in Science. John R. Gregg and F. T. C. Harris (eds.). Dordrecht, Holland: D. Reidel Publishing Company, 1964.

Frank, Philipp. *Philosophy of Science, the Link between Science and Philosophy.* Englewood Cliffs, N.J.: Prentice-Hall, Inc., 1951.

General Education in a Free Society. Report of the Harvard Committee. Cambridge, Mass.: Harvard University Press, 1945.

Glennan, T. Keith. "New Order of Technological Challenge," *Vital Speeches,* XXVI (February 1, 1960), 236–239.

Huxley, Julian. "The Future of Man," *Bulletin of the Atomic Scientist,* XV (December 1959), 401–404.

Killian, James R., Jr. "Problems in Science Teaching in the United States," in *The Challenge of Science Education.* Joseph S. Roucek (ed.). New York: Philosophical Library, 1959.

Komisar, B. Paul, and James E. McClellan. "The Logic of Slogans," in *Language and Concepts in Education.* B. Othanel Smith and Robert H. Ennis (eds.). Chicago: Rand McNally & Company, 1961, pp. 195–215.

Langer, Susanne K. *Philosophy in a New Key.* New York: The New American Library, 1958.

Margenau, Henry. *The Nature of Physical Reality, a Philosophy of Modern Physics.* New York: McGraw-Hill Book Company, Inc., 1950.

Mather, K. F. "Scientists' Responsibility for the Interpretation of Concepts to Laymen," *Science,* CXIX (March 5, 1954), 199–300.

Morrison, Robert S. "Where Is Biology Taking Us?" *Science,* CLV (January 27, 1967), 430–433.

Oppenheimer, Robe t. *Science and the Modern Mind.* Boston: Beacon Press, 1958, p. 76.

Phenix, Philip H. "Key Concepts and the Crisis in Learning," *Teachers College Record,* LVIII (December 1956), 137–143.

Piel, Gerard. "The Revolution in Man's Labor," *Bulletin of the Atomic Scientist,* XV (September 1959), 278–283.

Robinson, James T. *An Investigation of Selected Frameworks of Science,* unpublished doctoral dissertation. Stanford University, Stanford, Calif. 1964.

Schwab, Joseph J. "The Teaching of Science as Inquiry," *Bulletin of the Atomic Scientist,* XIV (November 1958), 374–379.

————. "Inquiry, the Science Teacher, and the Educator," *School Review,* LXVIII, No. 2 (1960), 176–195.

————. "The Structure of the Disciplines," a working paper prepared for the Project on Instruction of the National Education Association, June 1961. (Mimeographed.)

Schwab, Joseph J., and Paul F. Brandwein. *The Teaching of Science.* Cambridge, Mass.: Harvard University Press, 1962.

"Science in the Kindergarten and Early Grades," *Science Education News* (American Association for the Advancement of Science, Misc. Pub. No. 63-20, November 1963).

Seaborg, Glenn T. "The Chemical Education Materials Study," *Chemical Education Materials Study Newsletter,* I, No. 1 (November 1960), 1.

Semenov, N. "The Future of Man in the Atomic Age," *Bulletin of the Atomic Scientist,* XV (March 1959), 123–126.

Strong, Laurence E. "Facts, Students, Ideas," *Journal of Chemical Education,* XXXIX (March 1962), 126–129.

The Structure of Knowledge and the Curriculum. G. W. Ford and Lawrence Pugno (eds.). Chicago: Rand McNally & Company, 1964.

Toulmin, Stephen. *The Philosophy of Science, an Introduction.* New York: Harper & Row Publishers, Inc., Harper Torchbooks/The Science Library, 1960.

White, Stephen. "The Physical Science Study Committee, (3) The Planning and Structure of the Course," *Contemporary Physics,* II (October 1960), 39–54.

Woodger, J. H. *Biology and Language, an Introduction to the Methodology of the Biological Sciences Including Medicine.* New York: Cambridge University Press, 1952.

INDEX

Adaptation, 120–121
Adrian, E. D., 8
Analogy (*see also* Discovery):
  role in science, 86, 117, 134, 135,
    138
Aristotle:
  causality, 15
  force, 15
  four causes, 15
  intelligible principles, 75–76
  mechanics, 15
  ontology, 16
  organismic view, 20

Beckner, Morton, 95–101, 115,
  120, 122, 130
Becoming, *see* Organisms, history
Behaving, *see* Organisms, function
Being, *see* Organisms, structure
Biological explanation (*see also*
  Description):
  autonomy of, 27, 95–97, 115,
    120, 130–131
  causality, 122
  functional, 131
  genetic, 100
  historical, 95–96, 122
  lack of conceptualization in,
    103–104
  limitations of, 125, 130
  models, *see* Models
  phylogenetic, 100
  teleological, 95, 98, 99, 100, 122
  theoretical statements, 90–94
  theory, 100–101
Biological organization, 95–96,
  108–109
  directiveness, 96–100

Biological organization (continued)
  levels of, 96, 97, 99, 104–105,
    109, 120
Bohr, Niels, 77
Boole-Frege movement, 91, 120,
  122, 135
Bronowski, Jacob, 9
Bridgman, Percy, 34, 51, 52, 82–
  89, 114
Bruner, Jerome, 4, 140

Carnap, Rudolf, 51, 57
Causality, 54–57 (*see also* Biological explanation)
  Aristotle, 15, 29
  characteristics of, 55–56
  Democritus, 15
  Humean, 55
  Middle Ages, 15
  partial causes, 15, 56
  in physical description, 54
  prediction, 56
  principal of, 24, 28–29, 54, 56–
    57
  in quantum mechanics, 29–30,
    54–55
Causal laws, 87–89, 132, 136
  definitions and, 53–54
  definition of, 28–29, 57, 87, 117
  invariance, 57
  relation to constructs, 29, 54
  relation to states, 39, 48–49
C field, 40–42, 53, 71, 72, 116, 117,
  118, 119
Common sense, 76, 86, 127
Concepts(*see also* Constructs):
  acceptance of, 88
  biological, 96, 97, 99, 105

145